**FC&A**

# *Super Life, Super Health*

# *Engagement Calendar 2003*

## Publisher's Note

These health tips do not constitute medical advice and should not be construed as such. We cannot guarantee the safety or effectiveness of any treatment or advice mentioned. Some of these tips may not be effective for everyone.

A good doctor is the best judge of what medical treatment may be needed for certain conditions and diseases. We recommend in all cases that you contact your personal doctor or health care provider before taking or discontinuing any medications or before treating yourself in any way.

*"The LORD is my light and my salvation; whom shall I fear? The LORD is the defense of my life; whom shall I dread?"*

*Psalm 27:1*

FC&A Publishing
103 Clover Green
Peachtree City, GA 30269

**First printing September 2002**

ISBN 1-890957-65-8

| December | | | | | | | | January | | | | | | | | February | | | | | | |
|---|---|---|---|---|---|---|---|---|---|---|---|---|---|---|---|---|---|---|---|---|---|---|
| S | M | T | W | T | F | S | | S | M | T | W | T | F | S | | S | M | T | W | T | F | S |
| 1 | 2 | 3 | 4 | 5 | 6 | 7 | | | | 1 | 2 | 3 | 4 | | | | | | | | 1 |
| 8 | 9 | 10 | 11 | 12 | 13 | 14 | | 5 | 6 | 7 | 8 | 9 | 10 | 11 | | 2 | 3 | 4 | 5 | 6 | 7 | 8 |
| 15 | 16 | 17 | 18 | 19 | 20 | 21 | | 12 | 13 | 14 | 15 | 16 | 17 | 18 | | 9 | 10 | 11 | 12 | 13 | 14 | 15 |
| 22 | 23 | 24 | 25 | 26 | 27 | 28 | | 19 | 20 | 21 | 22 | 23 | 24 | 25 | | 16 | 17 | 18 | 19 | 20 | 21 | 22 |
| 29 | 30 | 31 | | | | | | 26 | 27 | 28 | 29 | 30 | 31 | | | 23 | 24 | 25 | 26 | 27 | 28 |

# January

*A wise man should consider that health is the greatest of human blessings, and learn how by his own thought to derive benefit from his illnesses. — Hippocrates*

## 30 Monday

## 31 Tuesday
*New Year's Eve*

## 1 Wednesday
*New Year's Day*

## 2 Thursday

## 3 Friday

*Take a break from white rice with high-fiber, hearty grains like kasha, couscous, bulgur, barley, wild rice, and millet. Check out cookbooks for recipe ideas — like couscous with chopped raisins, dried apricots, and a few toasted almonds.*

# January  2003

## 4 Saturday

## 5 Sunday

## Notes:

## Mega-mineral builds a better heart

Not enough magnesium in your diet could increase your risk of heart attack and high blood pressure. Besides helping your heart muscle, your body needs magnesium to help produce energy; build strong bones and teeth; and use calcium, vitamin D, and potassium. As you age, it may become more difficult to absorb and use the magnesium in your diet, making it a challenge to get the Dietary Reference Intake (DRI) of 320 to 420 milligrams (mg) for adults. So make wise food choices, especially since this mighty mineral is easily lost during washing, peeling, and processing. These supercharged foods make excellent choices:

| | |
|---|---|
| Avocado, 1/2 medium | 103 mg |
| Wheat germ, toasted, 1 oz | 90 mg |
| Almonds, dry roasted, 1 oz | 86 mg |
| Pinto beans, boiled, 1 cup | 95 mg |

| December | January | February |
|---|---|---|
| S M T W T F S | S M T W T F S | S M T W T F S |
| 1 2 3 4 5 6 7 | 1 2 3 4 | 1 |
| 8 9 10 11 12 13 14 | 5 6 7 8 9 10 11 | 2 3 4 5 6 7 8 |
| 15 16 17 18 19 20 21 | 12 13 14 15 16 17 18 | 9 10 11 12 13 14 15 |
| 22 23 24 25 26 27 28 | 19 20 21 22 23 24 25 | 16 17 18 19 20 21 22 |
| 29 30 31 | 26 27 28 29 30 31 | 23 24 25 26 27 28 |

# January

*The average American eats approximately 156 pounds of refined sugar every year.*

## 6 Monday

## 7 Tuesday

## 8 Wednesday

## 9 Thursday

## 10 Friday

*Tell depression to take a hike! Depression is the most common type of mental illness, affecting about one in 20 people. Exercise therapy can reduce stress and improve self-image. It also triggers the release of endorphins, giving you an attitude boost.*

# January  2003

## 11 Saturday

## 12 Sunday

## Notes:

## Keep your kidneys stone free — naturally

Your kidneys perform an essential job — filtering waste from your blood and removing it from your body as urine. But a kidney stone can form when the balance of liquids and dissolved solids in your kidneys are out of whack.

Nearly 70 to 80 percent of kidney stones contain calcium oxalate or calcium phosphate. These chemical compounds are part of your normal diet. Calcium oxalate is found in foods like spinach, tomatoes, peanuts, coffee, tea, and chocolate.

But another nutrient, calcium, can help you stay stone free. When you eat high-calcium foods with high-oxalate foods, the calcium keeps your body from absorbing the oxalate. This makes you less likely to form oxalate-based kidney stones.

However, don't load up on calcium supplements — you might actually increase your risk of kidney stones. Your best bet is to get calcium naturally by eating dairy foods; small bony fish, like sardines; and legumes.

| December | | | | | | | | January | | | | | | | | February | | | | | | |
|---|---|---|---|---|---|---|---|---|---|---|---|---|---|---|---|---|---|---|---|---|---|---|
| S | M | T | W | T | F | S | | S | M | T | W | T | F | S | | S | M | T | W | T | F | S |
| 1 | 2 | 3 | 4 | 5 | 6 | 7 | | | | 1 | 2 | 3 | 4 | | | | | | | | 1 |
| 8 | 9 | 10 | 11 | 12 | 13 | 14 | | 5 | 6 | 7 | 8 | 9 | 10 | 11 | | 2 | 3 | 4 | 5 | 6 | 7 | 8 |
| 15 | 16 | 17 | 18 | 19 | 20 | 21 | | 12 | 13 | 14 | 15 | 16 | 17 | 18 | | 9 | 10 | 11 | 12 | 13 | 14 | 15 |
| 22 | 23 | 24 | 25 | 26 | 27 | 28 | | 19 | 20 | 21 | 22 | 23 | 24 | 25 | | 16 | 17 | 18 | 19 | 20 | 21 | 22 |
| 29 | 30 | 31 | | | | | | 26 | 27 | 28 | 29 | 30 | 31 | | | 23 | 24 | 25 | 26 | 27 | 28 | |

# January

*"… and the fruit thereof shall be for meat, and the leaf thereof for medicine."*— *Ezekiel 47:12*

## 13 Monday

## 14 Tuesday

## 15 Wednesday

## 16 Thursday

## 17 Friday

*If you want to keep your heart healthy, eat fish more often. A large study on male doctors found that those who ate at least one fish meal a week were 52 percent less likely to die from a sudden heart attack than those who ate fish less than once a month.*

# January  2003

*"If you eat a handful of walnuts a day, you will lower your blood cholesterol, and therefore lower your cardiovascular risk," says Dr. Emilio Ros. He substituted walnuts for other fatty foods in the Mediter-ranean diet during a study, proving the diet change can lower the risk of heart disease by 11 percent.*

## 18 Saturday

## 19 Sunday

## Notes:

## Get a grip on tension headaches

The feeling is sometimes described as wearing a tight band around your head. That throbbing pain is probably a tension headache. While tension headaches don't usually last long, they can come back quite often. Try these helpful tips to keep them away.

- De-stress your life as much as you can. If you feel yourself stressing out, practice relaxation techniques.
- Get regular exercise. It's a great stress-buster and good for you in many other ways, too.
- Ease a tension headache with massage. Sit still with your eyes closed and rub your sore head. Work your fingers over your temples and forehead or wherever you feel pain. Rub your shoulders and neck to release the tightness that stress inflicts on your body. Breathe slowly and deeply and concentrate on relaxing.
- Get relief with aspirin or ibuprofen. A recent study shows that combining aspirin with caffeine may do an even better job of stopping a tension headache.
- Apply heating or cooling pads to your head, whichever is more comfortable.
- Take a nap. Sometimes sleep is the only thing that will interrupt the pain cycle.

| December | | | | | | | January | | | | | | | February | | | | | | |
|---|---|---|---|---|---|---|---|---|---|---|---|---|---|---|---|---|---|---|---|---|
| S | M | T | W | T | F | S | S | M | T | W | T | F | S | S | M | T | W | T | F | S |
| 1 | 2 | 3 | 4 | 5 | 6 | 7 | | | | 1 | 2 | 3 | 4 | | | | | | | 1 |
| 8 | 9 | 10 | 11 | 12 | 13 | 14 | 5 | 6 | 7 | 8 | 9 | 10 | 11 | 2 | 3 | 4 | 5 | 6 | 7 | 8 |
| 15 | 16 | 17 | 18 | 19 | 20 | 21 | 12 | 13 | 14 | 15 | 16 | 17 | 18 | 9 | 10 | 11 | 12 | 13 | 14 | 15 |
| 22 | 23 | 24 | 25 | 26 | 27 | 28 | 19 | 20 | 21 | 22 | 23 | 24 | 25 | 16 | 17 | 18 | 19 | 20 | 21 | 22 |
| 29 | 30 | 31 | | | | | 26 | 27 | 28 | 29 | 30 | 31 | | 23 | 24 | 25 | 26 | 27 | 28 | |

# January

*A slice of whole-grain bread is a fiber, mineral, and vitamin powerhouse, containing magnesium, zinc, folic acid, vitamin E, vitamin B6, and chromium. And it tastes pretty good, too!*

## 20 Monday
*Martin Luther King, Jr. Day*

## 21 Tuesday

## 22 Wednesday

## 23 Thursday

## 24 Friday

*Drinking large amounts of coffee or tea — even decaffeinated — can hinder your body's ability to absorb thiamin, an important B vitamin. Thiamin is essential for turning protein, fat, and carbohydrates into energy. It's also necessary for proper cell growth and transmitting nerve signals to the brain.*

# January  2003

*Do you have leg pain or cramping in your calf muscles, even after a short walk? As many people age, their legs don't get an adequate blood supply because of hardened or blocked blood vessels. This painful condition is called intermittent claudication, and the herb ginkgo may relieve these symptoms.*

## 25 Saturday

## 26 Sunday

## Notes:

## Heartburn help from man's best friend

Dogs may be smarter than people when it comes to soothing an upset stomach. When a dog's stomach hurts, it finds bitter grass to eat. That's pretty smart since bitter herbs help get digestive juices flowing.

Some people have too much stomach acid, and some have too little — especially older people. If you don't have enough acid, your food may sit undigested in your stomach too long, causing pain. To fight this kind of indigestion, eat bitter plants like watercress, endive, dandelion, artichokes, and grated orange peel (but not the fruit).

Ginger, a bitter spice, has been used for centuries to treat indigestion. Steep a teaspoon of grated ginger in hot water for 10 minutes, and drink throughout the day as needed. Chamomile tea, another ancient remedy, settles the stomach and helps digestion. Drink a cup between meals three or four times a day. Be careful if you are allergic to ragweed. You might also be allergic to chamomile.

| December | January | February |
|---|---|---|
| S M T W T F S | S M T W T F S | S M T W T F S |
| 1 2 3 4 5 6 7 |     1 2 3 4 |        1 |
| 8 9 10 11 12 13 14 | 5 6 7 8 9 10 11 | 2 3 4 5 6 7 8 |
| 15 16 17 18 19 20 21 | 12 13 14 15 16 17 18 | 9 10 11 12 13 14 15 |
| 22 23 24 25 26 27 28 | 19 20 21 22 23 24 25 | 16 17 18 19 20 21 22 |
| 29 30 31 | 26 27 28 29 30 31 | 23 24 25 26 27 28 |

# January

*"To lengthen thy life, lessen thy meals."*
*— Benjamin Franklin*

## 27 Monday

## 28 Tuesday

## 29 Wednesday

## 30 Thursday

## 31 Friday

*Vitamin E is available in most vegetable oils, but heating the oil to a high temperature destroys it. So if your food choices mainly consist of fried or highly processed foods, you're not getting the benefit of this powerful antioxidant.*

# February  2003

## 1 Saturday

## 2 Sunday
*Groundhog Day*

## Do you need more of this lifesaving mineral?

Your very life depends on a delicate balance of potassium in your cells. Your heartbeat, your breathing, and other vital organ functions require the right amount of potassium for regulation. Are you at risk for a potassium deficiency? Take this easy quiz and find out.

- Are you over age 55?
- Do you drink more than three cups of coffee a day?
- Do you regularly engage in vigorous activities that require a lot of endurance?
- Do you take laxatives once a week or more?
- Do you smoke?
- Have you recently had surgery or been through a very stressful experience?
- Have you recently been severely injured or burned?
- Do you take water pills (diuretics), digitalis, or cortisone drugs?
- Have you had part of your gastrointestinal tract removed?

If you answered yes to more than one question, you may have a potassium deficiency. Ask your doctor if you need potassium supplements. Remember — never take potassium supplements without your doctor's approval. Overdosing on potassium can be deadly.

| January | February | March |
|---|---|---|
| S M T W T F S | S M T W T F S | S M T W T F S |
| 1 2 3 4 | 1 | 1 |
| 5 6 7 8 9 10 11 | 2 3 4 5 6 7 8 | 2 3 4 5 6 7 8 |
| 12 13 14 15 16 17 18 | 9 10 11 12 13 14 15 | 9 10 11 12 13 14 15 |
| 19 20 21 22 23 24 25 | 16 17 18 19 20 21 22 | 16 17 18 19 20 21 22 |
| 26 27 28 29 30 31 | 23 24 25 26 27 28 | 23 24 25 26 27 28 29 |
| | | 30 31 |

# February

*"When the head aches, all the body is the worse." — English proverb*

## 3 Monday

## 4 Tuesday

## 5 Wednesday

## 6 Thursday

## 7 Friday

*Being overweight may increase your cancer risk. An extra 10 pounds can increase a woman's risk of breast cancer by almost 25 percent, and an extra 20 pounds more than doubles the risk. Overweight men are 50 to 70 percent more likely to develop prostate cancer and colorectal cancer than other men.*

# February  2003

*Just 40 minutes a week of moderate exercise can reduce your risk of developing Type 2 diabetes. In a Finnish study, that level of exercise reduced men's diabetes risk by 50 percent compared with nonexercisers.*

## 8 Saturday

## 9 Sunday

## Notes:

## Fight heart disease with folic acid

A simple vitamin deficiency could be responsible for 40 percent of heart attacks and strokes suffered by American men. The vitamin is folic acid or folate, a member of the B-vitamin family.

Dozens of studies show that folic acid reduces the level of homocysteine in the blood. Homocysteine, an amino acid, can cause narrowing of the arteries, leading to an increased risk of heart disease and stroke. Homocysteine could be responsible for many unexplained deaths in people who are otherwise healthy. Researchers estimate that if people would increase their daily intake of folic acid to 400 micrograms, as many as 50,000 deaths a year from heart disease could be prevented.

Folic acid is found in green leafy vegetables, like spinach and Romaine lettuce. Other good sources include:

| | |
|---|---|
| Avocado | Orange juice |
| Lentils | Kidney beans |
| Black beans | Lima beans |
| Peas | Fortified cereal |

| January | | | | | | | | February | | | | | | | | March | | | | | | |
|---|---|---|---|---|---|---|---|---|---|---|---|---|---|---|---|---|---|---|---|---|---|---|
| S | M | T | W | T | F | S | | S | M | T | W | T | F | S | | S | M | T | W | T | F | S |
| | | 1 | 2 | 3 | 4 | | | | | | | | | 1 | | | | | | | | 1 |
| 5 | 6 | 7 | 8 | 9 | 10 | 11 | | 2 | 3 | 4 | 5 | 6 | 7 | 8 | | 2 | 3 | 4 | 5 | 6 | 7 | 8 |
| 12 | 13 | 14 | 15 | 16 | 17 | 18 | | 9 | 10 | 11 | 12 | 13 | 14 | 15 | | 9 | 10 | 11 | 12 | 13 | 14 | 15 |
| 19 | 20 | 21 | 22 | 23 | 24 | 25 | | 16 | 17 | 18 | 19 | 20 | 21 | 22 | | 16 | 17 | 18 | 19 | 20 | 21 | 22 |
| 26 | 27 | 28 | 29 | 30 | 31 | | | 23 | 24 | 25 | 26 | 27 | 28 | | | 23 | 24 | 25 | 26 | 27 | 28 | 29 |
| | | | | | | | | | | | | | | | | 30 | 31 | | | | | |

# February

*Aim for excellence, not perfection. Perfectionists are 75 percent more likely to get sick than other people.*

## 10 Monday

## 11 Tuesday

## 12 Wednesday
*Lincoln's Birthday*

## 13 Thursday

## 14 Friday
*Valentine's Day*

---

*Temporomandibular joint disorder (TMJ) is often linked to teeth grinding or clenching, and it's easy to mistake for a simple earache. Before you go to the ear specialist, put your little finger into your ear canal with the fingernail facing toward the back. Open and close your jaw, feeling the movement of the temporomandibular joint. If this causes you a lot of discomfort, you may have TMJ.*

# February  2003

## 15 Saturday

## 16 Sunday

## Notes:

## Cancel out your cancer risk

You can lower your risk of several types of cancer by following these four simple rules.

**Eat more high-fiber foods.** The scientific community may not agree on how whole grains discourage cancer, but no one is arguing with the proof. About 95 percent of the research done on whole grains and cancer has produced positive results.

**Cut down on fatty foods.** A high-fat diet seems to put you more at risk for certain cancers. Researchers call fats "promoters" of cancer.

**Stay away from salt-cured, pickled, and smoked foods.** These foods contain nitrates, which may break down in your body to form cancer-causing compounds called nitrosamines.

**Load up on fruits and vegetables.** Plant food is rich in antioxidants, those powerful substances that fend off cancer, heart disease, and other serious diseases.

| January | February | March |
|---|---|---|
| S M T W T F S | S M T W T F S | S M T W T F S |
| 1 2 3 4 | 1 | 1 |
| 5 6 7 8 9 10 11 | 2 3 4 5 6 7 8 | 2 3 4 5 6 7 8 |
| 12 13 14 15 16 17 18 | 9 10 11 12 13 14 15 | 9 10 11 12 13 14 15 |
| 19 20 21 22 23 24 25 | 16 17 18 19 20 21 22 | 16 17 18 19 20 21 22 |
| 26 27 28 29 30 31 | 23 24 25 26 27 28 | 23 24 25 26 27 28 29 |
| | | 30 31 |

# February

*Prescription drugs, such as asthma inhalers, and some over-the-counter drugs, such as diet pills and decongestants, can cause anxiety-like symptoms and intensify stress.*

## 17 Monday
*Presidents' Day*

## 18 Tuesday

## 19 Wednesday

## 20 Thursday

## 21 Friday

*A strong cup of tea, either warm or cold, makes a soothing gargle for a painful sore throat. The tannin in tea shrinks blood vessels and swollen tissue. Make your tea twice as strong as you do for drinking, and use it to gargle as often as you like.*

# February  2003

*Summertime isn't the only time you should drink lots of water. During cold months, your skin can become dry and your lips chapped. Drinking lots of water helps keep your lips and your skin cells moist and comfortable.*

## 22 Saturday
*Washington's Birthday*

## 23 Sunday

## Take the heat out of heartburn

It's called heartburn, but it has nothing to do with your heart. When stomach acid backs up into your esophagus, it feels like a three-alarm fire burning in your chest. Try these simple solutions to protect your esophagus so you won't get "burned" again.

**Stop smoking.** Nicotine increases your production of stomach acid, and cigarette smoke causes a temporary reduction in the strength of your esophageal valve, allowing that acid to back up into your esophagus.

**Avoid food triggers.** Keep a food diary to help you identify the foods that give you heartburn. Common food triggers include chocolate, peppermint, caffeine, and spicy foods.

**Eat small meals.** Try eating six small meals throughout the day instead of three large meals.

**Stand up straight.** Bending, stooping, or lying down after meals can force food and stomach acid into your esophagus.

**Keep it slim.** Excess weight may increase pressure in your abdominal area, which can make food more likely to back up into your esophagus.

**Wear loose-fitting clothes.** The pressure from tight clothing can force food upward, causing heartburn.

**Raise your head.** Put a 6-inch block under the head of your bed. You will have the force of gravity on your side by having your head higher than your stomach when you are lying down.

| January | | | | | | | | February | | | | | | | | March | | | | | | |
|---|---|---|---|---|---|---|---|---|---|---|---|---|---|---|---|---|---|---|---|---|---|---|
| S | M | T | W | T | F | S | | S | M | T | W | T | F | S | | S | M | T | W | T | F | S |
| | | | 1 | 2 | 3 | 4 | | | | | | | | 1 | | | | | | | | 1 |
| 5 | 6 | 7 | 8 | 9 | 10 | 11 | | 2 | 3 | 4 | 5 | 6 | 7 | 8 | | 2 | 3 | 4 | 5 | 6 | 7 | 8 |
| 12 | 13 | 14 | 15 | 16 | 17 | 18 | | 9 | 10 | 11 | 12 | 13 | 14 | 15 | | 9 | 10 | 11 | 12 | 13 | 14 | 15 |
| 19 | 20 | 21 | 22 | 23 | 24 | 25 | | 16 | 17 | 18 | 19 | 20 | 21 | 22 | | 16 | 17 | 18 | 19 | 20 | 21 | 22 |
| 26 | 27 | 28 | 29 | 30 | 31 | | | 23 | 24 | 25 | 26 | 27 | 28 | | | 23 | 24 | 25 | 26 | 27 | 28 | 29 |
| | | | | | | | | | | | | | | | | 30 | 31 | | | | | |

# February

*The eight foods most likely to cause allergic reactions in people are shellfish; peanuts; tree nuts like walnuts, cashews, pecans, and almonds; milk; eggs; fish; soybeans; and wheat.*

## 24 Monday

## 25 Tuesday

## 26 Wednesday

## 27 Thursday

## 28 Friday

*Drinking cranberry juice is a tried-and-true home remedy to prevent urinary tract infections (UTIs). If you can't tolerate the taste of cranberry juice, try taking a vitamin C supplement. Like cranberry juice, it makes your urine more acidic. This helps prevent the growth of bacteria and infection.*

# March

# 2003

*Too much caffeine can make you jittery, but a new study shows that a little caffeine may have the opposite effect. In the study, caffeine lowered tension while it increased feelings of happiness and calmness. When they tested participants on their ability to recall and process information and solve problems, they performed better with caffeine.*

## 1 Saturday

## 2 Sunday

## Notes:

## Get some exercise to sleep like a baby

Insomnia affects 20 to 40 percent of adults every year. Older adults are the most frequent sufferers, but the aliment can strike anyone. You can consider yourself an insomniac if you can't go to sleep, can't stay asleep, or wake up far too early in the morning.

Studies show that exercise may be all people need to fall asleep faster and sleep better. In one study, participants — who were ages 50 to 76 — had four workouts a week, two workouts of stretching, aerobics, and strength training and two workouts of brisk walking.

The results after four months showed that the exercisers fell asleep faster and slept for an hour longer each night. Researchers aren't sure why exercise helps so much, but they think it might be related to stress reduction.

If you find yourself staring at the ceiling instead of drifting off to sweet dreams, it may be time to exercise more.

| | February | | | | | | | March | | | | | | | April | | | | | |
|---|---|---|---|---|---|---|---|---|---|---|---|---|---|---|---|---|---|---|---|---|---|
| S | M | T | W | T | F | S | S | M | T | W | T | F | S | S | M | T | W | T | F | S |
| | | | | | | 1 | | | | | | | 1 | | | | 1 | 2 | 3 | 4 | 5 |
| 2 | 3 | 4 | 5 | 6 | 7 | 8 | 2 | 3 | 4 | 5 | 6 | 7 | 8 | 6 | 7 | 8 | 9 | 10 | 11 | 12 |
| 9 | 10 | 11 | 12 | 13 | 14 | 15 | 9 | 10 | 11 | 12 | 13 | 14 | 15 | 13 | 14 | 15 | 16 | 17 | 18 | 19 |
| 16 | 17 | 18 | 19 | 20 | 21 | 22 | 16 | 17 | 18 | 19 | 20 | 21 | 22 | 20 | 21 | 22 | 23 | 24 | 25 | 26 |
| 23 | 24 | 25 | 26 | 27 | 28 | | 23 | 24 | 25 | 26 | 27 | 28 | 29 | 27 | 28 | 29 | 30 | | | |
| | | | | | | | 30 | 31 | | | | | | | | | | | | |

# March

*Fingernails don't grow as fast after age 30, but this is a natural part of the aging process.*

## 3 Monday

## 4 Tuesday

## 5 Wednesday
*Ash Wednesday*

## 6 Thursday

## 7 Friday

*If you have arthritis, relaxing in a bathtub full of warm water may ease your aching joints, but drinking a glass of cool water may also help. Water helps cushion and lubricate your joints. You should drink at least eight glasses of water a day to help keep your joints gliding smoothly along.*

# March  St. Patty's Day    2003

*Curcumin, an ingredient in the spice turmeric, may help prevent asthma attacks by curbing the release of substances that cause asthma's wheezing and tightening of the chest. The usual supplement dose is 1.5 to 3 grams daily. The only known side effect from turmeric is occasional stomach upset.*

## 8 Saturday

## 9 Sunday

## Notes:

## Protect yourself from 'traveler's diarrhea'

If you eat food or drink water contaminated with bacteria, like *E. coli,* you're likely to get a bad case of diarrhea, nausea, and vomiting. It's not usually life-threatening, but it can certainly be uncomfortable. In fact, the illness is so common in popular vacation destinations like Mexico and Central and South America it's known as traveler's diarrhea. If you don't want to be the next victim of Montezuma's revenge, practice these travel tips:

- Don't use tap water for drinking or brushing your teeth. Buy bottled water.
- Before eating, clean your hands with packaged wipes or antiseptic cleanser, not tap water.
- Drink bottled water, boiled coffee or tea, carbonated drinks, beer, or wine only.
- Order your drinks without ice.
- Eat fruits, like bananas, you can peel yourself.
- Don't eat raw vegetables or salads. Eat thoroughly cooked, hot food.
- Buy food and drinks from reputable restaurants and hotels, not street vendors.
- Pack some bromelain, a pineapple enzyme that may block *E. coli.*

| February | | | | | | |
|---|---|---|---|---|---|---|
| S | M | T | W | T | F | S |
| | | | | | | 1 |
| 2 | 3 | 4 | 5 | 6 | 7 | 8 |
| 9 | 10 | 11 | 12 | 13 | 14 | 15 |
| 16 | 17 | 18 | 19 | 20 | 21 | 22 |
| 23 | 24 | 25 | 26 | 27 | 28 | |

| March | | | | | | |
|---|---|---|---|---|---|---|
| S | M | T | W | T | F | S |
| | | | | | | 1 |
| 2 | 3 | 4 | 5 | 6 | 7 | 8 |
| 9 | 10 | 11 | 12 | 13 | 14 | 15 |
| 16 | 17 | 18 | 19 | 20 | 21 | 22 |
| 23 | 24 | 25 | 26 | 27 | 28 | 29 |
| 30 | 31 | | | | | |

| April | | | | | | |
|---|---|---|---|---|---|---|
| S | M | T | W | T | F | S |
| | | 1 | 2 | 3 | 4 | 5 |
| 6 | 7 | 8 | 9 | 10 | 11 | 12 |
| 13 | 14 | 15 | 16 | 17 | 18 | 19 |
| 20 | 21 | 22 | 23 | 24 | 25 | 26 |
| 27 | 28 | 29 | 30 | | | |

# March

*Exposure to sunlight can protect you from prostate cancer by helping your body produce vitamin D. Get at least a half hour of sunlight every day.*

## 10 Monday

## 11 Tuesday

## 12 Wednesday

## 13 Thursday

## 14 Friday

*Several varieties of beans, especially red kidney beans, are poisonous in their raw state. The beans contain phytohaemagglutinin, which is toxic to people and animals. But soaking beans in water for at least five hours and cooking them in fresh water for at least 10 minutes will destroy the toxins.*

# March

# 2003

*If you're shaking, sweating, and feeling weak, you may be suffering from hypoglycemia or low blood sugar. The best treatment is to eat something containing sugar, like one-quarter cup of raisins, eight Lifesavers, or 6 ounces of a sugared soft drink or fruit juice. You should feel better in about 15 minutes.*

## 15 Saturday

## 16 Sunday

## Notes:

## Save your hearing with these tips

Any noise over 85 to 90 decibels is hazardous when you're exposed to it for several hours a day. The noise of a lawn mower is about 80 to 95 decibels and a power saw is even louder at 95 to 110 decibels. Very loud noises, such as firearms and fireworks, can cause "acoustic trauma," which means your ears are damaged immediately.

Be aware of these warning signs of hearing loss that may last a few minutes or a few days after exposure to loud noises:

- Ears feel full or under pressure.

- Voices sound muffled and far away.

- You hear a ringing sound in your ears when all is quiet.

Remember, a noise is too loud and may cause hearing loss if you have to shout to be heard above the noise, you can't understand a person speaking to you when they are less than 2 feet away, or a person standing next to you can hear sounds from the stereo headphones you're wearing.

| February | | | | | | | | March | | | | | | | | April | | | | | | |
|---|---|---|---|---|---|---|---|---|---|---|---|---|---|---|---|---|---|---|---|---|---|---|
| S | M | T | W | T | F | S | | S | M | T | W | T | F | S | | S | M | T | W | T | F | S |
| | | | | | | 1 | | | | | | | | 1 | | | | 1 | 2 | 3 | 4 | 5 |
| 2 | 3 | 4 | 5 | 6 | 7 | 8 | | 2 | 3 | 4 | 5 | 6 | 7 | 8 | | 6 | 7 | 8 | 9 | 10 | 11 | 12 |
| 9 | 10 | 11 | 12 | 13 | 14 | 15 | | 9 | 10 | 11 | 12 | 13 | 14 | 15 | | 13 | 14 | 15 | 16 | 17 | 18 | 19 |
| 16 | 17 | 18 | 19 | 20 | 21 | 22 | | 16 | 17 | 18 | 19 | 20 | 21 | 22 | | 20 | 21 | 22 | 23 | 24 | 25 | 26 |
| 23 | 24 | 25 | 26 | 27 | 28 | | | 23 | 24 | 25 | 26 | 27 | 28 | 29 | | 27 | 28 | 29 | 30 | | | |
| | | | | | | | | 30 | 31 | | | | | | | | | | | | | |

# March

*Even toiletries labeled "unscented" include something to mask the unpleasant chemical smells. If you are sensitive to fragrances, look for "fragrance-free" on the package.*

## 17 Monday
*St. Patrick's Day*

## 18 Tuesday

## 19 Wednesday

## 20 Thursday

## 21 Friday
*Spring begins*

*Want a simple, safe, yet inexpensive treatment for diarrhea? Boil some rice. Scientists have discovered a substance in cooked rice that keeps your intestinal cells from producing too much chloride, which can cause diarrhea. In some countries, they simply drink the cooled water left in the pot after cooking rice.*

# March

# 2003

*Grow cabbage, carrots, celery, onions, and borage near your tomatoes to keep pests away, add flavor to the tomatoes, and return nutrients to the soil.*

## 22 Saturday

## 23 Sunday

## Notes:

## Simple way to burn extra calories

You burn extra calories for at least an hour — and sometimes several hours — after exercising. This is called afterburn or excess postexercise oxygen consumption. Unfortunately, people who are obese don't get the same afterburn benefits as people who are not obese.

Here's how afterburn works. For about two hours after you exercise, your tired muscles need glycogen, their source of energy. Carbohydrates and even candy bars eaten after exercising will be more easily converted to glycogen instead of being stored as fat.

But don't eat before exercising vigorously. Exercising on a full stomach can give you a stomachache. You'll probably find you need an empty stomach to jog or do a hard workout.

| February | | | | | | | March | | | | | | | April | | | | | | |
|---|---|---|---|---|---|---|---|---|---|---|---|---|---|---|---|---|---|---|---|---|
| S | M | T | W | T | F | S | S | M | T | W | T | F | S | S | M | T | W | T | F | S |
| | | | | | | 1 | | | | | | | 1 | | | 1 | 2 | 3 | 4 | 5 |
| 2 | 3 | 4 | 5 | 6 | 7 | 8 | 2 | 3 | 4 | 5 | 6 | 7 | 8 | 6 | 7 | 8 | 9 | 10 | 11 | 12 |
| 9 | 10 | 11 | 12 | 13 | 14 | 15 | 9 | 10 | 11 | 12 | 13 | 14 | 15 | 13 | 14 | 15 | 16 | 17 | 18 | 19 |
| 16 | 17 | 18 | 19 | 20 | 21 | 22 | 16 | 17 | 18 | 19 | 20 | 21 | 22 | 20 | 21 | 22 | 23 | 24 | 25 | 26 |
| 23 | 24 | 25 | 26 | 27 | 28 | | 23 | 24 | 25 | 26 | 27 | 28 | 29 | 27 | 28 | 29 | 30 | | | |
| | | | | | | | 30 | 31 | | | | | | | | | | | | |

# March

*Experiment with herbs and spices as a substitute for fat — and the salt shaker. Try rosemary with peas, dill with green beans, oregano with zucchini, or basil with tomatoes.*

## 24 Monday

## 25 Tuesday

## 26 Wednesday

## 27 Thursday

## 28 Friday

*The ancient practice of aromatherapy uses several oils to relieve anxiety. Bergamot, cedarwood, frankincense, geranium, hyssop, lavender, sandalwood, and ylang ylang are a few of them. Dilute them in your bath or combine them with a massage oil for a relaxing rub.*

# March

St. Patty's Day

# 2003

## 29 Saturday

## 30 Sunday

## Notes:

## Turn on the lights to end depression

Feeling sad? Craving starchy foods and sweets? Gaining weight? You may be suffering from winter depression, also known as SAD (seasonal affective disorder). Symptoms, like daytime drowsiness, fatigue, and diminished concentration, appear late in November and disappear by the following April. SAD affects four times as many women as men.

Researchers have found a treatment to help make the "blues" disappear. It involves bright lights every morning or evening for a week or two during winter. Morning exposure seems to produce the greatest relief.

Apparently, some SAD sufferers have a delayed secretion of melatonin, a hormone that regulates sleep, at night. The eye's sensitivity to light may be a factor in winter depression. The retinas of people with SAD seem to have difficulty getting more light out of the shorter winter days.

If you think winter depression is getting you down, talk with your doctor about SAD and light therapy.

| March | | | | | | |
|S|M|T|W|T|F|S|
| | | | | | |1|
|2|3|4|5|6|7|8|
|9|10|11|12|13|14|15|
|16|17|18|19|20|21|22|
|23|24|25|26|27|28|29|
|30|31| | | | | |

| April | | | | | | |
|S|M|T|W|T|F|S|
| |1|2|3|4|5| |
|6|7|8|9|10|11|12|
|13|14|15|16|17|18|19|
|20|21|22|23|24|25|26|
|27|28|29|30| | | |

| May | | | | | | |
|S|M|T|W|T|F|S|
| | | | |1|2|3|
|4|5|6|7|8|9|10|
|11|12|13|14|15|16|17|
|18|19|20|21|22|23|24|
|25|26|27|28|29|30|31|

# April

*Evening walks with your family will give you an opportunity to talk about the day's events. You'll become a closer family and more physically fit.*

## 31 Monday

## 1 Tuesday
*April Fool's Day*

## 2 Wednesday

## 3 Thursday

## 4 Friday

*To replace electrolytes — salt and minerals found in your body's tissues — after a bout with diarrhea, mix one teaspoon of salt and four teaspoons of sugar into one quart of water. Drink two cups of this mixture every hour.*

# April

# 2003

*Wash away your allergy troubles. After outdoor activities, take a quick shower and shampoo your hair to remove any pollen residue. Your hair can harbor a lot of pollen, especially if it's long.*

## 5 Saturday

## 6 Sunday
*Daylight Saving Time begins*

## Notes:

## Ancient algae protects prostate

*Dunaliella bardawil* is a remarkable alga. It's so tough it can survive the harsh environment of the Dead Sea. What's more, many health experts think it could help you avoid prostate cancer. *Dunaliella bardawil* contains high levels of beta carotene, a carotenoid that is converted into vitamin A in your body. A recent study found that men with the lowest levels of beta carotene were 45 percent more likely to develop prostate cancer than men with the highest levels. *Dunaliella bardawil* also contains lycopene, another prostate-protecting carotenoid.

Beta carotene protects your health in many ways, including boosting your immune system. In one study, however, smokers who took beta carotene supplements were more likely to develop lung cancer.

Eating fresh, whole foods, like carrots, spinach, and sweet potatoes, is the best way to get beta carotene. Yet, beta carotene supplements made from natural sources, like *Dunaliella bardawil,* may be healthier than synthetic supplements.

| March | | | | | | | | April | | | | | | | | May | | | | | | |
|---|---|---|---|---|---|---|---|---|---|---|---|---|---|---|---|---|---|---|---|---|---|---|
| S | M | T | W | T | F | S | | S | M | T | W | T | F | S | | S | M | T | W | T | F | S |
| | | | | | | 1 | | | | 1 | 2 | 3 | 4 | 5 | | | | | | | 1 | 2 | 3 |
| 2 | 3 | 4 | 5 | 6 | 7 | 8 | | 6 | 7 | 8 | 9 | 10 | 11 | 12 | | 4 | 5 | 6 | 7 | 8 | 9 | 10 |
| 9 | 10 | 11 | 12 | 13 | 14 | 15 | | 13 | 14 | 15 | 16 | 17 | 18 | 19 | | 11 | 12 | 13 | 14 | 15 | 16 | 17 |
| 16 | 17 | 18 | 19 | 20 | 21 | 22 | | 20 | 21 | 22 | 23 | 24 | 25 | 26 | | 18 | 19 | 20 | 21 | 22 | 23 | 24 |
| 23 | 24 | 25 | 26 | 27 | 28 | 29 | | 27 | 28 | 29 | 30 | | | | | 25 | 26 | 27 | 28 | 29 | 30 | 31 |
| 30 | 31 | | | | | | | | | | | | | | | | | | | | | |

# April

*If you are diabetic, a relatively unknown B vitamin called biotin may reduce the amount of insulin your body needs. You can get biotin naturally from liver, egg yolks, and cereals.*

## 7 Monday

## 8 Tuesday

## 9 Wednesday

## 10 Thursday

## 11 Friday

*A sore throat can be a real headache. So why not fight it with aspirin? Dissolve two aspirin tablets in warm water and gargle. You'll feel hours of soothing relief. Just make sure you don't use coated aspirin tablets or acetaminophen.*

# April

# 2003

*If you suffer from sleep apnea, get it treated. You could gain a good night's sleep and perhaps lose some inches around your middle. According to a recent study, people treated for the disorder lost abdominal fat. Researchers think it's possible more sleep altered their metabolism favorably.*

## 12 Saturday

## 13 Sunday
*Palm Sunday*

## Notes:

## Positive outlook pumps up immune system

People with cancer who are relaxed and optimistic about their chances of survival live longer than anxious people trying to cope with cancer on their own, according to researchers at the University of California at Los Angeles.

For the same reason, your chances of surviving a heart attack are better if you have emotional support. In one study of heart attack victims, those with supporting companions and family members had better survival rates and less severe heart problems than people without support.

A group of people ages 60 to 70 gave their immune system a boost by living in a resort facility for 11 days and learning about exercise, diet, stress management, and changing their lifestyle. Blood samples were taken before and after the program. The people who reported feeling less stress after the program had increased levels of the disease-fighting white blood cells in their bodies.

| | March | | | | | | | | April | | | | | | | | May | | | | | |
|---|---|---|---|---|---|---|---|---|---|---|---|---|---|---|---|---|---|---|---|---|---|---|
| S | M | T | W | T | F | S | S | M | T | W | T | F | S | S | M | T | W | T | F | S |
| | | | | | | 1 | | | 1 | 2 | 3 | 4 | 5 | | | | | 1 | 2 | 3 |
| 2 | 3 | 4 | 5 | 6 | 7 | 8 | 6 | 7 | 8 | 9 | 10 | 11 | 12 | 4 | 5 | 6 | 7 | 8 | 9 | 10 |
| 9 | 10 | 11 | 12 | 13 | 14 | 15 | 13 | 14 | 15 | 16 | 17 | 18 | 19 | 11 | 12 | 13 | 14 | 15 | 16 | 17 |
| 16 | 17 | 18 | 19 | 20 | 21 | 22 | 20 | 21 | 22 | 23 | 24 | 25 | 26 | 18 | 19 | 20 | 21 | 22 | 23 | 24 |
| 23 | 24 | 25 | 26 | 27 | 28 | 29 | 27 | 28 | 29 | 30 | | | | 25 | 26 | 27 | 28 | 29 | 30 | 31 |
| 30 | 31 | | | | | | | | | | | | | | | | | | | |

# April

*Cellulose, found in the strings of celery and outer skins of corn kernels, is an insoluble fiber. Insoluble fiber helps move food more quickly through your digestive system.*

## 14 Monday

## 15 Tuesday
*Tax returns due*

## 16 Wednesday

## 17 Thursday
*Passover*

## 18 Friday
*Good Friday*

*On the day after you "spring ahead" for Daylight Saving Time, you are five times more likely to have a car accident. That's because the highways are buzzing with sleep-deprived drivers. If you adjust gradually to the time change — go to sleep a little earlier and wake up a little earlier each day — you're more likely to be alert.*

# April  2003

*Although green tea has less caffeine than black tea, too much of this good thing might keep you awake at night. If this is true for you, switch to a decaffeinated tea, either green or black, that will still give you super antioxidant protection without this side effect.*

## 19 Saturday

## 20 Sunday
*Easter*

## Notes:

## Unbeatable way to get vitamin C

Many people take supplements containing mega-doses of vitamin C, as much as 1,000 milligrams (mg) a day or more. Although too much vitamin C probably won't kill you, large doses can cause kidney stones, nausea, abdominal cramps, and diarrhea.

A recent study found that your body has trouble absorbing more than 400 mg at a time, and you lose the rest in your urine. To make matters worse, chewable vitamin C tablets can erode your tooth enamel.

You can easily get the recommended amount of vitamin C — 75 mg for women and 90 mg for men — if you eat at least five fruits and vegetables a day. So before you invest a lot of money in mega-dose supplements, eat more of these delicious foods:

| | |
|---|---|
| sweet red peppers | orange juice |
| green peppers | strawberries |
| cantaloupe | brussels sprouts |
| grapefruit | broccoli |

| March | | | | | | |
|---|---|---|---|---|---|---|
| S | M | T | W | T | F | S |
| | | | | | | 1 |
| 2 | 3 | 4 | 5 | 6 | 7 | 8 |
| 9 | 10 | 11 | 12 | 13 | 14 | 15 |
| 16 | 17 | 18 | 19 | 20 | 21 | 22 |
| 23 | 24 | 25 | 26 | 27 | 28 | 29 |
| 30 | 31 | | | | | |

| April | | | | | | |
|---|---|---|---|---|---|---|
| S | M | T | W | T | F | S |
| | | 1 | 2 | 3 | 4 | 5 |
| 6 | 7 | 8 | 9 | 10 | 11 | 12 |
| 13 | 14 | 15 | 16 | 17 | 18 | 19 |
| 20 | 21 | 22 | 23 | 24 | 25 | 26 |
| 27 | 28 | 29 | 30 | | | |

| May | | | | | | |
|---|---|---|---|---|---|---|
| S | M | T | W | T | F | S |
| | | | | 1 | 2 | 3 |
| 4 | 5 | 6 | 7 | 8 | 9 | 10 |
| 11 | 12 | 13 | 14 | 15 | 16 | 17 |
| 18 | 19 | 20 | 21 | 22 | 23 | 24 |
| 25 | 26 | 27 | 28 | 29 | 30 | 31 |

# April

*Cooked tomatoes provide as much as five times more lycopene than fresh tomatoes. Lycopene in your diet can lower your risk of heart disease and certain types of cancer.*

## 21 Monday

## 22 Tuesday
*Earth Day*

## 23 Wednesday

## 24 Thursday

## 25 Friday
*National Arbor Day*

*If you need a way to chill out at the end of the day and relieve stress, you don't have to go any farther than your own yard. Gazing at flowers and trees can relieve stress, lower blood pressure, and relax tense muscles.*

# April  2003

*Sunlight may help you combat pesky dust mites, a cause of allergy symptoms. A study in Australia found that leaving mite-infested rugs outside for four hours on a hot, sunny day killed 100 percent of mites and their eggs. This would probably work for bedding, curtains, and pillows as well.*

## 26 Saturday

## 27 Sunday

## Notes:

## What to do when you overdo

Tendons are strong cords of fiber that connect your muscles to your bones or to other muscles. When they become inflamed, you have tendinitis. Don't let tendinitis put a crimp in your activities. A little extra care will keep you going strong.

**Rest.** You need to give those inflamed tendons time to heal. Don't make your problem worse by working through your pain.

**Put it on ice.** Ice prevents swelling and relieves pain. Wrap a towel around an ice pack to protect your skin, and don't apply ice for more than 15 minutes at a time.

**Heat it up.** If you already have swelling, heat may work better than ice. The warmth increases blood flow, which speeds healing. Use an electric heating pad; take a hot bath; or apply hot, wet towels to the painful area.

**Ease the pain.** Aspirin and ibuprofen can help reduce pain and inflammation.

| March | | | | | | | April | | | | | | | May | | | | | | |
|---|---|---|---|---|---|---|---|---|---|---|---|---|---|---|---|---|---|---|---|---|
| S | M | T | W | T | F | S | S | M | T | W | T | F | S | S | M | T | W | T | F | S |
| | | | | | | 1 | | | 1 | 2 | 3 | 4 | 5 | | | | | | 1 | 2 | 3 |
| 2 | 3 | 4 | 5 | 6 | 7 | 8 | 6 | 7 | 8 | 9 | 10 | 11 | 12 | 4 | 5 | 6 | 7 | 8 | 9 | 10 |
| 9 | 10 | 11 | 12 | 13 | 14 | 15 | 13 | 14 | 15 | 16 | 17 | 18 | 19 | 11 | 12 | 13 | 14 | 15 | 16 | 17 |
| 16 | 17 | 18 | 19 | 20 | 21 | 22 | 20 | 21 | 22 | 23 | 24 | 25 | 26 | 18 | 19 | 20 | 21 | 22 | 23 | 24 |
| 23 | 24 | 25 | 26 | 27 | 28 | 29 | 27 | 28 | 29 | 30 | | | | 25 | 26 | 27 | 28 | 29 | 30 | 31 |
| 30 | 31 | | | | | | | | | | | | | | | | | | | |

# April

*Presoak beans in water for eight hours before cooking — and then throw away the water — to reduce the complex sugars responsible for the troublesome gas-producing properties of beans.*

## 28 Monday

## 29 Tuesday

## 30 Wednesday

## 1 Thursday
*May Day*

## 2 Friday

*Inactivity increases bone loss. Try to engage in weight-bearing exercises such as walking, bicycling, or aerobics three to four hours a week. Exercising and strengthening your back muscles can help correct or prevent "dowager's hump." Exercise will also strengthen your muscles, making falls less likely.*

# May  2003

*A product claiming to be a good source of a certain vitamin, mineral, fiber, or other nutrient must contain 10 to 19 percent of that item. A high source food contains at least 20 percent of the recommended Daily Value.*

## 3 Saturday

## 4 Sunday

## Notes:

## Soothing comfort for canker sores

A canker sore begins as a small blister, which bursts and becomes encircled by bright red inflammation. It usually heals on its own within two weeks. In the meantime, there are ways to make yourself more comfortable and help speed the healing process.

**Avoid irritating foods.** Salty, acidic, spicy, or abrasive foods can aggravate mouth sores. Avoid foods like tomatoes, citrus fruits, nuts, salsa, and chips.

**Brush gently.** Don't scrub your gums and avoid damaging the protective membrane that covers the sore.

**Soothe with home remedies.** Apply milk of magnesia, a paste made with baking soda and water, or Pepto-Bismol to the sore.

**Visit your pharmacy.** Several over-the-counter ointments have numbing or waterproofing properties to make you feel better and speed healing.

**See your dentist.** A jagged tooth, braces, or dentures could make your canker sore even worse. Make sure there is no irritant in your mouth to prolong your discomfort.

| April | May | June |
|---|---|---|
| S M T W T F S | S M T W T F S | S M T W T F S |
| 1 2 3 4 5 | 1 2 3 | 1 2 3 4 5 6 7 |
| 6 7 8 9 10 11 12 | 4 5 6 7 8 9 10 | 8 9 10 11 12 13 14 |
| 13 14 15 16 17 18 19 | 11 12 13 14 15 16 17 | 15 16 17 18 19 20 21 |
| 20 21 22 23 24 25 26 | 18 19 20 21 22 23 24 | 22 23 24 25 26 27 28 |
| 27 28 29 30 | 25 26 27 28 29 30 31 | 29 30 |

# May

*You can avoid the "ouch" of pulling off an adhesive bandage by soaking the bandage top and edges in baby oil before removing it.*

## 5 Monday
*Cinco de Mayo*

## 6 Tuesday

## 7 Wednesday

## 8 Thursday

## 9 Friday

*The next time you're feeling blue, dip into the deep blue sea for your dinner. New medical evidence suggests that the omega-3 fatty acids found in fish — called docosahexaenoic acid (DHA) and eicosapentaenoic acid (EPA) — can help drive away depression.*

# May  2003

*The first thing to do when you've been stung by a bee or wasp is to scrape out the stinger with a knife or credit card. Don't pull it out. That can make it worse. Make a paste of meat tenderizer and water. Apply it to the bite to help break down the venom.*

## 10 Saturday

## 11 Sunday
*Mother's Day*

## Notes:

## Secrets to soothe itchy skin

A general itchy feeling may mean you've got a rash, but it could also be a warning sign of a more serious condition, like kidney failure, liver disease, hyperthyroidism, or Hodgkin's disease. Drug reactions, insect bites, dry skin, and contact with fiberglass insulation or fabrics can also cause an itchy reaction. Until you determine the source of your itch, try these tips:

- Bathe with lukewarm water and a mild soap.
- Pat your skin dry rather than rubbing it.
- Don't bathe more often than once a day.
- Use a moisturizer after a bath.
- Apply an ice pack to the itchy area.
- Try lotions containing menthol.
- Take an antihistamine if you think you are having an allergic reaction.
- Avoid steroid creams. They can cause side effects.
- Run a humidifier in your home.

| | April | | | | | | | | May | | | | | | | | June | | | | | |
|---|---|---|---|---|---|---|---|---|---|---|---|---|---|---|---|---|---|---|---|---|---|---|---|
| S | M | T | W | T | F | S | S | M | T | W | T | F | S | S | M | T | W | T | F | S |
| | | 1 | 2 | 3 | 4 | 5 | | | | | 1 | 2 | 3 | | | | | | | |
| 6 | 7 | 8 | 9 | 10 | 11 | 12 | 4 | 5 | 6 | 7 | 8 | 9 | 10 | 1 | 2 | 3 | 4 | 5 | 6 | 7 |
| 13 | 14 | 15 | 16 | 17 | 18 | 19 | 11 | 12 | 13 | 14 | 15 | 16 | 17 | 8 | 9 | 10 | 11 | 12 | 13 | 14 |
| 20 | 21 | 22 | 23 | 24 | 25 | 26 | 18 | 19 | 20 | 21 | 22 | 23 | 24 | 15 | 16 | 17 | 18 | 19 | 20 | 21 |
| 27 | 28 | 29 | 30 | | | | 25 | 26 | 27 | 28 | 29 | 30 | 31 | 22 | 23 | 24 | 25 | 26 | 27 | 28 |
| | | | | | | | | | | | | | | 29 | 30 | | | | | |

# May

*To avoid food-borne illness, thoroughly cook poultry and other meats. Never cut fruits and vegetables with the same knife or on the same cutting board as raw meat.*

## 12 Monday

## 13 Tuesday

## 14 Wednesday

## 15 Thursday

## 16 Friday

*Practice progressive relaxation for 20 minutes twice a day to relieve high blood pressure and other physiological responses to stress. Tighten and release each muscle group in turn, starting with the soles of your feet and slowly working up to your scalp.*

# May

# 2003

*"If you are cold, tea will warm you; if you are too heated, it will cool you;*
*if you are depressed, it will cheer you; if you are excited, it will calm you."*
*— William Gladstone, former British Prime Minister*

## 17 Saturday

## 18 Sunday

## Notes:

## The trouble with broccoli

Scientists say some people have more taste buds than others and are more sensitive to flavors, especially bitter or sweet. People can be divided into three categories: nontasters, about 25 percent of the population; medium tasters, about 50 percent; and super-tasters, about 25 percent. People who are super-tasters have more taste buds per square centimeter of tongue surface compared with nontasters. It's the super-tasters who may be most bothered by the taste of broccoli and other bitter foods, like cabbage and grapefruit.

If you choose to eat broccoli, consider the cooking method. If you want to get vitamin C, it's best to munch on raw spears. You get somewhat less vitamin C when fresh broccoli is cooked, and a lot less when you eat frozen, cooked broccoli. If you want lots of beta carotene, choose frozen, cooked broccoli. For getting the most fiber, eat it any way you like. Broccoli's fiber content isn't affected by cooking.

| April | | | | | | | | May | | | | | | | | June | | | | | | |
|---|---|---|---|---|---|---|---|---|---|---|---|---|---|---|---|---|---|---|---|---|---|---|
| S | M | T | W | T | F | S | | S | M | T | W | T | F | S | | S | M | T | W | T | F | S |
| | | 1 | 2 | 3 | 4 | 5 | | | | | | 1 | 2 | 3 | | 1 | 2 | 3 | 4 | 5 | 6 | 7 |
| 6 | 7 | 8 | 9 | 10 | 11 | 12 | | 4 | 5 | 6 | 7 | 8 | 9 | 10 | | 8 | 9 | 10 | 11 | 12 | 13 | 14 |
| 13 | 14 | 15 | 16 | 17 | 18 | 19 | | 11 | 12 | 13 | 14 | 15 | 16 | 17 | | 15 | 16 | 17 | 18 | 19 | 20 | 21 |
| 20 | 21 | 22 | 23 | 24 | 25 | 26 | | 18 | 19 | 20 | 21 | 22 | 23 | 24 | | 22 | 23 | 24 | 25 | 26 | 27 | 28 |
| 27 | 28 | 29 | 30 | | | | | 25 | 26 | 27 | 28 | 29 | 30 | 31 | | 29 | 30 | | | | | |

# May

*Wash clothes, bedding, and curtains in hot water (at least 130 degrees F) to kill a major cause of allergy symptoms — dust mites.*

## 19 Monday

## 20 Tuesday

## 21 Wednesday

## 22 Thursday

## 23 Friday

*Try this self-help exercise if you want to stop grinding your teeth while asleep. Clench your teeth for five seconds, then relax your jaw for five seconds. Do this exercise five times in a row, six times a day, for two weeks.*

# May

# 2003

*Rub some rubbing alcohol on a mosquito bite. It will stop the itching and make the bite disappear. If you want to stop mosquitoes from biting you in the first place, splash some rubbing alcohol on yourself and let it dry before you go outside.*

## 24 Saturday

## 25 Sunday

## Notes:

## Take the heat out of painful burns

First- and second-degree burns smaller than a silver dollar on an adult and smaller than a quarter on a child can usually be treated at home. Larger burns should be examined by a doctor.

**First-degree burns.** The skin is red and turns white when touched. Sunburn is the most common cause of first-degree burns.

- Apply cold water to the burn as quickly as possible, but don't use ice!
- Cover the burn loosely with gauze, and let it begin healing on its own for at least 24 hours before applying lotions or ointments.

**Second-degree burns.** These burns often cause blistering. The more superficial second-degree burns look white and whitish-red, and they feel wet or waxy dry to the touch.

- Soak burned area in cool water, then gently dry the burn with a clean towel.
- Apply antibiotic cream to the burned area and cover with a nonstick dressing. Wash off and reapply the antibiotic cream two or three times a day.

| April | | | | | | | | May | | | | | | | | June | | | | | | |
|---|---|---|---|---|---|---|---|---|---|---|---|---|---|---|---|---|---|---|---|---|---|---|
| S | M | T | W | T | F | S | | S | M | T | W | T | F | S | | S | M | T | W | T | F | S |
| | | 1 | 2 | 3 | 4 | 5 | | | | | | 1 | 2 | 3 | | 1 | 2 | 3 | 4 | 5 | 6 | 7 |
| 6 | 7 | 8 | 9 | 10 | 11 | 12 | | 4 | 5 | 6 | 7 | 8 | 9 | 10 | | 8 | 9 | 10 | 11 | 12 | 13 | 14 |
| 13 | 14 | 15 | 16 | 17 | 18 | 19 | | 11 | 12 | 13 | 14 | 15 | 16 | 17 | | 15 | 16 | 17 | 18 | 19 | 20 | 21 |
| 20 | 21 | 22 | 23 | 24 | 25 | 26 | | 18 | 19 | 20 | 21 | 22 | 23 | 24 | | 22 | 23 | 24 | 25 | 26 | 27 | 28 |
| 27 | 28 | 29 | 30 | | | | | 25 | 26 | 27 | 28 | 29 | 30 | 31 | | 29 | 30 | | | | | |

# May

*According to a recent study, people who ate salmon every day were 50 percent less likely to get diabetes as people who didn't eat salmon.*

## 26 Monday
### Memorial Day

## 27 Tuesday

## 28 Wednesday

## 29 Thursday

## 30 Friday

*If you carry your wallet in your back pocket, it can put too much pressure on nerves and muscles when you sit down. Clean out those business and credit cards you don't use and start carrying your billfold in your front pocket.*

# June

# 2003

*You know certain creams can help relieve the itching, burning, and swelling of hemorrhoids. But hemorrhoid cream can also be used on your face to fight wrinkles, puffy eyes, and a saggy jaw line. Give this unusual treatment a try. Just be careful not to get any in your eyes.*

## 31 Saturday

## 1 Sunday

## Notes:

## Exercise can end knee pain

Your thigh muscle holds your kneecap firmly against your knee, except when you completely straighten your leg. The kneecap doesn't slip from side to side because it's connected to a tendon that runs in a groove at the end of the thigh bone.

If your thigh muscle becomes weak, that tendon can slip out of the groove, and your kneecap moves around, causing a painful, swollen knee.

Exercising your thigh muscles is important if you've had a cast on your leg, injured your knee, or were confined to bed for several days. Check with your doctor or physical therapist before exercising.

These no-stress knee exercises can help rebuild your strength.

- Lying on your back, tighten your thigh muscle. Hold tight for 10 seconds, then relax for 10 seconds. Repeat 10 times.

- Lie on the floor and place a rolled towel under your knee. Straighten your leg, then return to resting position. Do three sets of 10.

| May | | | | | | | June | | | | | | | July | | | | | | |
|---|---|---|---|---|---|---|---|---|---|---|---|---|---|---|---|---|---|---|---|---|
| S | M | T | W | T | F | S | S | M | T | W | T | F | S | S | M | T | W | T | F | S |
| | | | | 1 | 2 | 3 | 1 | 2 | 3 | 4 | 5 | 6 | 7 | | | 1 | 2 | 3 | 4 | 5 |
| 4 | 5 | 6 | 7 | 8 | 9 | 10 | 8 | 9 | 10 | 11 | 12 | 13 | 14 | 6 | 7 | 8 | 9 | 10 | 11 | 12 |
| 11 | 12 | 13 | 14 | 15 | 16 | 17 | 15 | 16 | 17 | 18 | 19 | 20 | 21 | 13 | 14 | 15 | 16 | 17 | 18 | 19 |
| 18 | 19 | 20 | 21 | 22 | 23 | 24 | 22 | 23 | 24 | 25 | 26 | 27 | 28 | 20 | 21 | 22 | 23 | 24 | 25 | 26 |
| 25 | 26 | 27 | 28 | 29 | 30 | 31 | 29 | 30 | | | | | | 27 | 28 | 29 | 30 | 31 | | |

# June

*Studies show that certain foods can bring on asthma attacks. Some of the more common foods linked to asthma flare-ups are shellfish, soy, wheat, nuts, eggs, fish, chocolate, and milk.*

## 2 Monday

## 3 Tuesday

## 4 Wednesday

## 5 Thursday

## 6 Friday

*Try sucking on a lemon wedge if you get queasy in a car or on a boat. It should quickly ease your discomfort. Ginger is a natural remedy, too. You can buy ginger supplements at any natural food store. Or try candied or crystallized ginger.*

# June  2003

*Protect yourself from squamous cell skin cancer by adding lemon to your food. The key to lemons' anti-cancer power may be d-limonene, a chemical that gives citrus fruits their smell. It's mostly in the zest, so you'll need to shave off this outermost, colored section of the peel to get the cancer fighter.*

## 7 Saturday

## 8 Sunday

## Notes:

## Warm up to exercise

Many people think stretching before exercise is a good way to warm up. Unfortunately, stretching cold muscles can actually cause an injury. The best way to warm up is to start the activity gradually. If you run, begin by walking. If you swim, begin with leisurely laps, slowly getting faster. This gradual increase warms up the specific muscles you'll be using during your exercise. You will need to warm up more in cold weather and less in hot weather. If you plan to exercise outdoors in cold weather, try warming up inside so you won't have to remove extra clothing as you get warmer.

And don't forget to cool down after exercising. Sudden inactivity after vigorous exercise can cause blood to pool, especially in your legs. This could lead to lightheadedness and decreased blood flow to your heart.

| May | | | | | | | | June | | | | | | | July | | | | | |
| S | M | T | W | T | F | S | S | M | T | W | T | F | S | S | M | T | W | T | F | S |
| --- | --- | --- | --- | --- | --- | --- | --- | --- | --- | --- | --- | --- | --- | --- | --- | --- | --- | --- | --- | --- |
| | | | | 1 | 2 | 3 | 1 | 2 | 3 | 4 | 5 | 6 | 7 | | | 1 | 2 | 3 | 4 | 5 |
| 4 | 5 | 6 | 7 | 8 | 9 | 10 | 8 | 9 | 10 | 11 | 12 | 13 | 14 | 6 | 7 | 8 | 9 | 10 | 11 | 12 |
| 11 | 12 | 13 | 14 | 15 | 16 | 17 | 15 | 16 | 17 | 18 | 19 | 20 | 21 | 13 | 14 | 15 | 16 | 17 | 18 | 19 |
| 18 | 19 | 20 | 21 | 22 | 23 | 24 | 22 | 23 | 24 | 25 | 26 | 27 | 28 | 20 | 21 | 22 | 23 | 24 | 25 | 26 |
| 25 | 26 | 27 | 28 | 29 | 30 | 31 | 29 | 30 | | | | | | 27 | 28 | 29 | 30 | 31 | | |

# June

*Just 3 ounces of liver has 331 milligrams of cholesterol, which is more than the recommended maximum daily amount for a healthy diet.*

## 9 Monday

## 10 Tuesday

## 11 Wednesday

## 12 Thursday

## 13 Friday

*Here's a simple way to get rid of corns and calluses without spending a lot of bread. In fact, you'll only need one slice. Just tape a piece of stale bread soaked in vinegar over your corn or callus and keep it on overnight. You can substitute a piece of cloth for the bread and get the same amazing results.*

# June  2003

*If you've had a cold or throat infection, your toothbrush might be a home for lingering germs. Instead of throwing away a barely used toothbrush, dump a teaspoon of bleach in a glass of cold water. Soak your toothbrush in the glass for about 15 minutes, then rinse well.*

## 14 Saturday
*Flag Day*

## 15 Sunday
*Father's Day*

## Notes:

## Getting the most from your eye drops

Here's how you can get the maximum benefits and fewest side effects from eye drops.

- Wash and dry hands before applying medicine.
- Check medicine for expiration date, discoloration, or contamination.
- Tilt head back. Gently pull down lower eyelid with index finger. Using the same hand, place middle finger alongside the inside corner of eye and apply slight pressure.
- Hold medicine container above eye. Squeeze recommended number of drops into eye. If you have trouble telling if you are getting drops in your eye, store the eye drops in the refrigerator. The cold sensation will make it easier to tell how many drops have been administered.
- After applying drops, wait a few seconds. Then look down and lift lower eyelid to touch upper eyelid.
- Release eyelid, but keep eyes closed for about two minutes. Blink several times to spread medicine over entire eye.
- Do not allow tip of medicine bottle to touch eye.

| | May | | | | | | | | June | | | | | | | | July | | | | | |
|---|---|---|---|---|---|---|---|---|---|---|---|---|---|---|---|---|---|---|---|---|---|---|
| S | M | T | W | T | F | S | S | M | T | W | T | F | S | S | M | T | W | T | F | S |
| | | | | 1 | 2 | 3 | 1 | 2 | 3 | 4 | 5 | 6 | 7 | | | 1 | 2 | 3 | 4 | 5 |
| 4 | 5 | 6 | 7 | 8 | 9 | 10 | 8 | 9 | 10 | 11 | 12 | 13 | 14 | 6 | 7 | 8 | 9 | 10 | 11 | 12 |
| 11 | 12 | 13 | 14 | 15 | 16 | 17 | 15 | 16 | 17 | 18 | 19 | 20 | 21 | 13 | 14 | 15 | 16 | 17 | 18 | 19 |
| 18 | 19 | 20 | 21 | 22 | 23 | 24 | 22 | 23 | 24 | 25 | 26 | 27 | 28 | 20 | 21 | 22 | 23 | 24 | 25 | 26 |
| 25 | 26 | 27 | 28 | 29 | 30 | 31 | 29 | 30 | | | | | | 27 | 28 | 29 | 30 | 31 | | |

# June

*Bilberries, the European variety of the blueberry, can sharpen your vision and help your eyes adjust from light to darkness.*

## 16 Monday

## 17 Tuesday

## 18 Wednesday

## 19 Thursday

## 20 Friday

*Don't wait until you're thirsty to drink water. The switch that runs the thirst center in your brain doesn't even wake up until you're already dehydrated. As you get older, your thirst switch becomes even more forgetful. So keep a water bottle handy and sip whether you're thirsty or not.*

# June  2003

*If your hemorrhoids flare up, you might not have time to drive to the store for special ointment.*
*Soothe the itching and burning with apple cider vinegar. Just soak a cotton ball in the vinegar*
*and dab it where you need relief. If the vinegar stings, use half-vinegar, half-water instead.*

## 21 Saturday
*Summer begins*

## 22 Sunday

## Notes:

## Focus on food to prevent vision loss

A simple wall calendar may keep you from going blind. Just place your hand over one eye and look at the calendar. Do the lines look broken, distorted, or wavy? Now try the other eye. If you are over age 50, use the calendar to test your eyes every day.

Age-related macular degeneration (ARMD) is the most common cause of vision loss in people over 50. The macula is located in the center of the retina. After 50 or 60 years, the macula can begin to break down, causing your central vision to become blurry.

Since high blood pressure and heart disease are risk factors for ARMD, if you cut the fat, especially saturated fat, from your diet, you'll be ahead of the game. Then eat lots of dark-green, leafy vegetables. One study found that people who ate the most collard greens and spinach had a lower rate of macular degeneration.

| May | | | | | | | | June | | | | | | | | July | | | | | | |
|---|---|---|---|---|---|---|---|---|---|---|---|---|---|---|---|---|---|---|---|---|---|---|
| S | M | T | W | T | F | S | | S | M | T | W | T | F | S | | S | M | T | W | T | F | S |
| | | | | 1 | 2 | 3 | | 1 | 2 | 3 | 4 | 5 | 6 | 7 | | | | 1 | 2 | 3 | 4 | 5 |
| 4 | 5 | 6 | 7 | 8 | 9 | 10 | | 8 | 9 | 10 | 11 | 12 | 13 | 14 | | 6 | 7 | 8 | 9 | 10 | 11 | 12 |
| 11 | 12 | 13 | 14 | 15 | 16 | 17 | | 15 | 16 | 17 | 18 | 19 | 20 | 21 | | 13 | 14 | 15 | 16 | 17 | 18 | 19 |
| 18 | 19 | 20 | 21 | 22 | 23 | 24 | | 22 | 23 | 24 | 25 | 26 | 27 | 28 | | 20 | 21 | 22 | 23 | 24 | 25 | 26 |
| 25 | 26 | 27 | 28 | 29 | 30 | 31 | | 29 | 30 | | | | | | | 27 | 28 | 29 | 30 | 31 | | |

# June

*If you suffer from insomnia, try some honey. It boosts a chemical in your brain that calms you down and helps you sleep.*

## 23 Monday

## 24 Tuesday

## 25 Wednesday

## 26 Thursday

## 27 Friday

*Drinking a cup of coffee a day is linked with more sex for older women and more potency for older men, based on a questionnaire sent to Michigan residents age 60 and older. If research can prove this one, a trip to Starbucks may be just what the doctor orders.*

# June  2003

*If you don't like taking over-the-counter cough medicine, you can make your own natural cough syrup. Mix the juice of one lemon with two tablespoons of glycerine and 12 teaspoons of honey. Take one teaspoon every half hour, stirring before each use.*

## 28 Saturday

## 29 Sunday

## Notes:

## Handy hiccup relief

When you hiccup, your diaphragm contracts involuntarily. As you inhale, the space between the vocal cords closes quickly, interfering with the flow of air and causing the hiccup sound. Raising your carbon dioxide level helps reduce hiccup frequency. This may explain why holding your breath and other techniques designed to interrupt your respiratory rhythm work wonders.

Here are a few more remedies to try the next time you need hiccup relief.

- Eat some dry bread.
- Swallow some crushed ice.
- Tickle the top of your mouth with a cotton swab.

| | May | | | | | | | | June | | | | | | | | July | | | | | |
|---|---|---|---|---|---|---|---|---|---|---|---|---|---|---|---|---|---|---|---|---|---|---|---|
| S | M | T | W | T | F | S | S | M | T | W | T | F | S | S | M | T | W | T | F | S |
| | | | | | 1 | 2 | 3 | 1 | 2 | 3 | 4 | 5 | 6 | 7 | | | | 1 | 2 | 3 | 4 | 5 |
| 4 | 5 | 6 | 7 | 8 | 9 | 10 | 8 | 9 | 10 | 11 | 12 | 13 | 14 | 6 | 7 | 8 | 9 | 10 | 11 | 12 |
| 11 | 12 | 13 | 14 | 15 | 16 | 17 | 15 | 16 | 17 | 18 | 19 | 20 | 21 | 13 | 14 | 15 | 16 | 17 | 18 | 19 |
| 18 | 19 | 20 | 21 | 22 | 23 | 24 | 22 | 23 | 24 | 25 | 26 | 27 | 28 | 20 | 21 | 22 | 23 | 24 | 25 | 26 |
| 25 | 26 | 27 | 28 | 29 | 30 | 31 | 29 | 30 | | | | | | 27 | 28 | 29 | 30 | 31 | | |

# June

*Avoid cooking cauliflower in an iron or aluminum pot. The vegetable can turn brown or yellow if it comes in contact with these metals.*

## 30 Monday

## 1 Tuesday

## 2 Wednesday

## 3 Thursday

## 4 Friday
Independence Day

*You want to soften your rough cuticles, but who can afford a fancy manicure? Try this instead. Mix one cup of baby oil with a half cup of lemon juice. Heat the mixture slightly, then soak your fingers for about five minutes. You'll feel like you came right from the salon.*

# July

# 2003

*You remembered to wear sunscreen during your day in the sun, but you forgot to wear a hat. Now it feels like your scalp is on fire. To find soothing relief, brew a pot of green tea, let it cool, and rinse your hair with it after you shampoo.*

## 5 Saturday

## 6 Sunday

## Notes:

## Try RICE for ankle pain

Ever stepped off a curb and turned your ankle? If your ankle sprain is mild, you can ease the pain and keep the swelling down by using the RICE treatment — Rest, Ice, Compression, and Elevation.

- Stay off your feet for the first two days after you sprain your ankle.
- Put an ice pack on your ankle for about 20 minutes three or four times a day. Do not apply ice directly to your skin and avoid compressing the ankle area with ice.
- Wrap your ankle in an elastic bandage to control swelling and to support and protect it, especially if you must walk around. Don't wrap it so tightly your toes go numb or turn red.
- Prop up your swollen ankle above the level of your heart. Stretch out on your sofa with your foot on a pillow.
- Five to 10 times a day, do gentle exercises to strengthen the muscles supporting your ankle.

| June | | | | | | |
|---|---|---|---|---|---|---|
| S | M | T | W | T | F | S |
| 1 | 2 | 3 | 4 | 5 | 6 | 7 |
| 8 | 9 | 10 | 11 | 12 | 13 | 14 |
| 15 | 16 | 17 | 18 | 19 | 20 | 21 |
| 22 | 23 | 24 | 25 | 26 | 27 | 28 |
| 29 | 30 | | | | | |

| July | | | | | | |
|---|---|---|---|---|---|---|
| S | M | T | W | T | F | S |
| | | 1 | 2 | 3 | 4 | 5 |
| 6 | 7 | 8 | 9 | 10 | 11 | 12 |
| 13 | 14 | 15 | 16 | 17 | 18 | 19 |
| 20 | 21 | 22 | 23 | 24 | 25 | 26 |
| 27 | 28 | 29 | 30 | 31 | | |

| August | | | | | | |
|---|---|---|---|---|---|---|
| S | M | T | W | T | F | S |
| | | | | | 1 | 2 |
| 3 | 4 | 5 | 6 | 7 | 8 | 9 |
| 10 | 11 | 12 | 13 | 14 | 15 | 16 |
| 17 | 18 | 19 | 20 | 21 | 22 | 23 |
| 24 | 25 | 26 | 27 | 28 | 29 | 30 |
| 31 | | | | | | |

# July

*Make a refreshing, lower-calorie beverage by mixing fruit juice with seltzer water and crushed ice.*

## 7 Monday

## 8 Tuesday

## 9 Wednesday

## 10 Thursday

## 11 Friday

*Some studies have found that the trace mineral chromium is helpful in the treatment or prevention of diabetes. Reach for the whole grains at your local market to get your daily chromium, since the milling of grains to make white bread and rice removes up to 83 percent of the chromium.*

# July  2003

## 12 Saturday

## 13 Sunday

## Notes:

## Fight cancer with flavor

By adding flavor to your food, you could be doing your body a favor. Some familiar flavorings may help prevent cancer.

**Basil.** Fresh basil may add more than zesty flavor to your foods. It can help your body increase production of glutathione, a substance that zaps cancer-causing chemicals. Although further studies need to be done to confirm basil's cancer-fighting abilities, it's a delicious addition to your favorite dishes.

**Rosemary.** If you enjoy cooking with rosemary, you might be getting cancer protection as well. Rosemary is a strong antioxidant, and studies show it may help prevent breast cancer.

**Curry.** If your favorite restaurant serves spicy Indian food, count yourself lucky. It could be giving you extra cancer protection. Turmeric, the main ingredient in curry, contains a substance called curcumin that gives turmeric its yellow coloring. According to new research, curcumin may also help prevent the growth of colon tumors.

| June | | | | | | |
|---|---|---|---|---|---|---|
| S | M | T | W | T | F | S |
| 1 | 2 | 3 | 4 | 5 | 6 | 7 |
| 8 | 9 | 10 | 11 | 12 | 13 | 14 |
| 15 | 16 | 17 | 18 | 19 | 20 | 21 |
| 22 | 23 | 24 | 25 | 26 | 27 | 28 |
| 29 | 30 | | | | | |

| July | | | | | | |
|---|---|---|---|---|---|---|
| S | M | T | W | T | F | S |
| | | 1 | 2 | 3 | 4 | 5 |
| 6 | 7 | 8 | 9 | 10 | 11 | 12 |
| 13 | 14 | 15 | 16 | 17 | 18 | 19 |
| 20 | 21 | 22 | 23 | 24 | 25 | 26 |
| 27 | 28 | 29 | 30 | 31 | | |

| August | | | | | | |
|---|---|---|---|---|---|---|
| S | M | T | W | T | F | S |
| | | | | | 1 | 2 |
| 3 | 4 | 5 | 6 | 7 | 8 | 9 |
| 10 | 11 | 12 | 13 | 14 | 15 | 16 |
| 17 | 18 | 19 | 20 | 21 | 22 | 23 |
| 24 | 25 | 26 | 27 | 28 | 29 | 30 |
| 31 | | | | | | |

# July

*"Everything good is found in ginger."*
*— Ancient Indian proverb*

## 14 Monday

## 15 Tuesday

## 16 Wednesday

## 17 Thursday

## 18 Friday

*It's alive! Alive! Although baker's yeast isn't as frightening as Frankenstein's monster, it is a live organism. Make sure you wash your hands after baking bread or else you could be at risk for a yeast infection.*

# July  2003

*You had a great time camping — except for all the bug bites you brought home. Douse those itchy spots with a cotton ball soaked in vinegar. It should help relieve the itch.*

## 19 Saturday

## 20 Sunday

## Notes:

## Polish away fungus with boric acid

If one of your nails becomes thick and dull-looking, you may have a fungal infection. It isn't clear why these infections occur, although warm, moist locations may encourage them to spread.

Florida ranchers have an inexpensive home remedy for thick and dull-looking nails infected with a fungus. They fill a jar with water and 4 to 6 ounces of boric acid, then paint this mixture on their nails twice a day.

But you have to have patience to see this remedy work its magic. It can take up to six months to a year to work. The ranchers keep the jar filled with water and boric acid all year long. The exact amount of boric acid doesn't matter, but the jar should have about an inch of crystals at the bottom at all times.

| June |
|---|
| S M T W T F S |
| 1 2 3 4 5 6 7 |
| 8 9 10 11 12 13 14 |
| 15 16 17 18 19 20 21 |
| 22 23 24 25 26 27 28 |
| 29 30 |

| July |
|---|
| S M T W T F S |
| 1 2 3 4 5 |
| 6 7 8 9 10 11 12 |
| 13 14 15 16 17 18 19 |
| 20 21 22 23 24 25 26 |
| 27 28 29 30 31 |

| August |
|---|
| S M T W T F S |
| 1 2 |
| 3 4 5 6 7 8 9 |
| 10 11 12 13 14 15 16 |
| 17 18 19 20 21 22 23 |
| 24 25 26 27 28 29 30 |
| 31 |

# July

*Clip nails immediately after bathing when they're damp and soft to avoid problems.*

## 21 Monday

## 22 Tuesday

## 23 Wednesday

## 24 Thursday

## 25 Friday

*Relaxation techniques practiced for 10 to 20 minutes a day will help you feel calmer and more in control. Deep breathing is especially helpful. Close your eyes and focus on moving your stomach in and out as you breathe through your nose. Repeat until you're relaxed.*

# July

# 2003

*Several unusual oils may reduce joint inflammation in people with arthritis. These oils include evening primrose, flaxseed, and borage seed oils. Because these oils aren't found in foods you normally eat, you have to get them from supplements. The effective dose is 1 to 2 grams daily.*

## 26 Saturday

## 27 Sunday

## Notes:

## Eat peanuts to fight heart disease

In France, a country known for its fatty cooking sauces, there is a relatively low death rate from heart disease. Researchers believe this may be partly due to the French habit of drinking wine with meals. This has become known as the "French paradox," since a high-fat diet is usually associated with a higher risk of heart disease.

But did you know you can get the same protective benefits from eating an ounce of peanuts? Peanuts contain resveratrol, a phytochemical linked to reduced heart disease. This cholesterol-lowering compound is also found in wine and red grape juice. An ounce of peanuts has about 73 micrograms (mcg) of resveratrol compared with wine's 160 mcg.

Peanuts are also high in protein and fiber, and they're a good source of many vitamins and minerals, including vitamin E, niacin, manganese, folate, magnesium, and potassium.

| June | | | | | | |
|---|---|---|---|---|---|---|
| S | M | T | W | T | F | S |
| 1 | 2 | 3 | 4 | 5 | 6 | 7 |
| 8 | 9 | 10 | 11 | 12 | 13 | 14 |
| 15 | 16 | 17 | 18 | 19 | 20 | 21 |
| 22 | 23 | 24 | 25 | 26 | 27 | 28 |
| 29 | 30 | | | | | |

| July | | | | | | |
|---|---|---|---|---|---|---|
| S | M | T | W | T | F | S |
| | | 1 | 2 | 3 | 4 | 5 |
| 6 | 7 | 8 | 9 | 10 | 11 | 12 |
| 13 | 14 | 15 | 16 | 17 | 18 | 19 |
| 20 | 21 | 22 | 23 | 24 | 25 | 26 |
| 27 | 28 | 29 | 30 | 31 | | |

| August | | | | | | |
|---|---|---|---|---|---|---|
| S | M | T | W | T | F | S |
| | | | | | 1 | 2 |
| 3 | 4 | 5 | 6 | 7 | 8 | 9 |
| 10 | 11 | 12 | 13 | 14 | 15 | 16 |
| 17 | 18 | 19 | 20 | 21 | 22 | 23 |
| 24 | 25 | 26 | 27 | 28 | 29 | 30 |
| 31 | | | | | | |

# July

*Prepare your own nutritious "fruit-sicles." Combine fruit juice and small chunks of fruit, pour into a paper cup, add a popsicle stick, and freeze until firm.*

## 28 Monday

## 29 Tuesday

## 30 Wednesday

## 31 Thursday

## 1 Friday

*Lose that upper arm jiggle with this easy exercise. Sit in a straight-backed chair. Hold a weight in each hand and raise both arms over your head. Bend one elbow as you lower that hand behind your head. Raise it back overhead and repeat with the other arm. Keep alternating.*

# August  2003

## 2 Saturday

## 3 Sunday

## Notes:

## Tricks to evade ticks and Lyme disease

L yme disease is the most common insect-borne disease in the United States today. Here are some simple ways to protect yourself.

- Avoid wooded or grassy areas in the spring and summer.
- Do a thorough "tick check" of yourself and pet after being in a wooded or grassy area.
- Always wear shoes, long pants, and long sleeves if you have to go into a possible tick-infested area. Tuck your pant legs into your socks to prevent ticks from getting on your socks and crawling up into your pants.
- Use insect repellent, especially formulas containing the chemical DEET. Follow the manufacturer's instructions for application.
- Wear light-colored clothing of tightly woven material when you go into wooded or grassy areas. This makes it easier to see the ticks on your clothes and harder for the ticks to grab on.

| July | | | | | | | August | | | | | | | September | | | | | | |
|---|---|---|---|---|---|---|---|---|---|---|---|---|---|---|---|---|---|---|---|---|
| S | M | T | W | T | F | S | S | M | T | W | T | F | S | S | M | T | W | T | F | S |
| | | 1 | 2 | 3 | 4 | 5 | | | | | | 1 | 2 | | 1 | 2 | 3 | 4 | 5 | 6 |
| 6 | 7 | 8 | 9 | 10 | 11 | 12 | 3 | 4 | 5 | 6 | 7 | 8 | 9 | 7 | 8 | 9 | 10 | 11 | 12 | 13 |
| 13 | 14 | 15 | 16 | 17 | 18 | 19 | 10 | 11 | 12 | 13 | 14 | 15 | 16 | 14 | 15 | 16 | 17 | 18 | 19 | 20 |
| 20 | 21 | 22 | 23 | 24 | 25 | 26 | 17 | 18 | 19 | 20 | 21 | 22 | 23 | 21 | 22 | 23 | 24 | 25 | 26 | 27 |
| 27 | 28 | 29 | 30 | 31 | | | 24 | 25 | 26 | 27 | 28 | 29 | 30 | 28 | 29 | 30 | | | | |
| | | | | | | | 31 | | | | | | | | | | | | | |

# August

*Nix the nightcap. A glass of alcohol before you go to bed may help you drop off, but it could interfere with your normal sleep patterns and wake you up later.*

## 4 Monday

## 5 Tuesday

## 6 Wednesday

## 7 Thursday

## 8 Friday

*It's not just sunbathing on the beach that can lead to skin cancer. Now it seems the cheese dog and fries you eat at the beach may be just as bad for your skin. Studies show a high-fat diet may help cancer grow after the sun damages your skin cells.*

# August  2003

*Deep sleep kicks on the mechanisms in your pituitary gland to release a substance called human growth hormone (HGH). It is only during sleep that you can regenerate and repair skin, organs, and muscle tissue. Deep sleep may be the real fountain of youth and HGH the revitalizing spring.*

## 9 Saturday

## 10 Sunday

## Notes:

## Hidden danger in licorice

Did you know a seemingly harmless piece of black licorice can send your blood pressure skyrocketing? Though many people think black licorice containing glycyrrhizic acid is no longer available in the United States, many types of imported licorice still contain this flavoring. Glycyrrhizic acid may cause salt retention and potassium loss, which can lead to high blood pressure.

In searching for other blood pressure culprits, check your medicine cabinet. Some skin ointments, anti-hemorrhoidal creams, eye drops, and nasal sprays contain ingredients that can have the same effect as licorice. Diuretics, or water pills, which commonly appear in weight loss products, might also affect your blood pressure. And some over-the-counter painkillers, such as aspirin, ibuprofen, and naproxen, could make your blood pressure medication worthless.

Since many innocent items can affect blood pressure, let your doctor know about any medications and supplements you're taking.

| July | | | | | | | | August | | | | | | | | September | | | | | | |
|---|---|---|---|---|---|---|---|---|---|---|---|---|---|---|---|---|---|---|---|---|---|---|
| S | M | T | W | T | F | S | | S | M | T | W | T | F | S | | S | M | T | W | T | F | S |
| | | 1 | 2 | 3 | 4 | 5 | | | | | | | 1 | 2 | | | 1 | 2 | 3 | 4 | 5 | 6 |
| 6 | 7 | 8 | 9 | 10 | 11 | 12 | | 3 | 4 | 5 | 6 | 7 | 8 | 9 | | 7 | 8 | 9 | 10 | 11 | 12 | 13 |
| 13 | 14 | 15 | 16 | 17 | 18 | 19 | | 10 | 11 | 12 | 13 | 14 | 15 | 16 | | 14 | 15 | 16 | 17 | 18 | 19 | 20 |
| 20 | 21 | 22 | 23 | 24 | 25 | 26 | | 17 | 18 | 19 | 20 | 21 | 22 | 23 | | 21 | 22 | 23 | 24 | 25 | 26 | 27 |
| 27 | 28 | 29 | 30 | 31 | | | | 24 | 25 | 26 | 27 | 28 | 29 | 30 | | 28 | 29 | 30 | | | | |
| | | | | | | | | 31 | | | | | | | | | | | | | | |

# August

*Caffeine increases the pain-relieving effects of aspirin and ibuprofen. But don't buy special formulas of the pain relievers to get this boost. Simply take your pill with a caffeinated beverage.*

## 11 Monday

## 12 Tuesday

## 13 Wednesday

## 14 Thursday

## 15 Friday

*Benzoates are a type of preservative that can trigger asthma attacks in some people. Check labels for benzoic acid, sodium benzoate, butylated hydroxyanisole (BHA), or butylated hydroxytoluene (BHT). You'll find benzoates in bread, chocolate, fat, instant drink powders, jam, margarine, mayonnaise, oil, and soft drinks.*

# August  2003

*Eggplant is a high-fiber, low-calorie, fat-free food. Unfortunately, it also holds the record for absorbing fat faster than any other vegetable. Keep eggplant recipes low fat by not adding oil or butter. Wash and pierce the eggplant's skin and bake whole in a 400-degree oven for about 30 minutes.*

## 16 Saturday

## 17 Sunday

## Notes:

## Eat more often to lower cholesterol

Millions of people have given up many of their favorite foods in a valiant attempt to lower their cholesterol levels. One study suggests that combining a low-fat diet with a simple dietary trick could help lower your cholesterol levels even more.

The number of meals you eat a day is the magic behind this new trick. People who divided their food into nine meals a day helped lower total blood cholesterol by 6.5 percent and bad LDL cholesterol by 8.1 percent compared with the group eating the same amount of food but only eating three meals a day.

Eating nine meals a day can lower the risk of heart disease by about 12 percent. Remember that the people in the study eating nine meals a day did not eat more food or calories than the three-meals-a-day group. They just had smaller meals more often.

| July | | | | | | |
|---|---|---|---|---|---|---|
| S | M | T | W | T | F | S |
| | | 1 | 2 | 3 | 4 | 5 |
| 6 | 7 | 8 | 9 | 10 | 11 | 12 |
| 13 | 14 | 15 | 16 | 17 | 18 | 19 |
| 20 | 21 | 22 | 23 | 24 | 25 | 26 |
| 27 | 28 | 29 | 30 | 31 | | |

| August | | | | | | |
|---|---|---|---|---|---|---|
| S | M | T | W | T | F | S |
| | | | | | 1 | 2 |
| 3 | 4 | 5 | 6 | 7 | 8 | 9 |
| 10 | 11 | 12 | 13 | 14 | 15 | 16 |
| 17 | 18 | 19 | 20 | 21 | 22 | 23 |
| 24 | 25 | 26 | 27 | 28 | 29 | 30 |
| 31 | | | | | | |

| September | | | | | | |
|---|---|---|---|---|---|---|
| S | M | T | W | T | F | S |
| | 1 | 2 | 3 | 4 | 5 | 6 |
| 7 | 8 | 9 | 10 | 11 | 12 | 13 |
| 14 | 15 | 16 | 17 | 18 | 19 | 20 |
| 21 | 22 | 23 | 24 | 25 | 26 | 27 |
| 28 | 29 | 30 | | | | |

# August

*To get rid of dandruff naturally, rinse your hair with a mixture of three tablespoons of vinegar and a cup of water. Rinsing with lemon juice also helps.*

## 18 Monday

## 19 Tuesday

## 20 Wednesday

## 21 Thursday

## 22 Friday

*Mold causes many allergy symptoms. Clean areas in your home that tend to be damp, like under sinks and around toilets, with bleach and water. Houseplants and aquariums can also harbor mold. If you must have houseplants, buy a mold retardant from your local nursery.*

# August  2003

*Avocados contain large amounts of linoleic and linolenic acids. You can only get these two polyunsaturated fatty acids from your diet, yet they are necessary for important heart functions, like controlling blood pressure, blood clotting, and blood fat levels. One avocado provides more than half your daily requirement of linoleic acid.*

## 23 Saturday

## 24 Sunday

## Notes:

## Natural, better-than-aspirin pain relief

Want something that eases muscle inflammation and soreness better than aspirin — without any harsh side effects? Try vitamin C. This popular nutrient is making a name for itself squaring off against everyday muscle soreness. Vitamin C can also speed healing of more serious muscle injuries.

Your body needs vitamin C to make collagen. This crucial protein is in charge of building and repairing cartilage, ligaments, muscles, bones, and everything else that holds your body together.

And don't forget vitamin C is a top antioxidant. When your muscles are injured or inflamed, you need antioxidant protection more than ever. Infection and your body's natural healing process cause free radicals to build up in the damaged tissue. These renegade chemicals can cause even more harm — unless you send in vitamin C to sweep them away.

| July | | | | | | |
|---|---|---|---|---|---|---|
| S | M | T | W | T | F | S |
| | | 1 | 2 | 3 | 4 | 5 |
| 6 | 7 | 8 | 9 | 10 | 11 | 12 |
| 13 | 14 | 15 | 16 | 17 | 18 | 19 |
| 20 | 21 | 22 | 23 | 24 | 25 | 26 |
| 27 | 28 | 29 | 30 | 31 | | |

| August | | | | | | |
|---|---|---|---|---|---|---|
| S | M | T | W | T | F | S |
| | | | | | 1 | 2 |
| 3 | 4 | 5 | 6 | 7 | 8 | 9 |
| 10 | 11 | 12 | 13 | 14 | 15 | 16 |
| 17 | 18 | 19 | 20 | 21 | 22 | 23 |
| 24 | 25 | 26 | 27 | 28 | 29 | 30 |
| 31 | | | | | | |

| September | | | | | | |
|---|---|---|---|---|---|---|
| S | M | T | W | T | F | S |
| | 1 | 2 | 3 | 4 | 5 | 6 |
| 7 | 8 | 9 | 10 | 11 | 12 | 13 |
| 14 | 15 | 16 | 17 | 18 | 19 | 20 |
| 21 | 22 | 23 | 24 | 25 | 26 | 27 |
| 28 | 29 | 30 | | | | |

# August

*According to one study, by getting up off the couch and becoming involved in regular physical activity, you've lowered your risk of colon cancer by a whopping 83 percent.*

## 25 Monday

## 26 Tuesday

## 27 Wednesday

## 28 Thursday

## 29 Friday

*Rubbing salt in a wound adds to your agony. Yet, putting salt on a bee sting actually helps relieve the pain. Just wet the spot where you've been stung and pour some salt on it.*

# August  2003

*No matter how thoroughly you brush your teeth, you're still missing spots. In fact, you're missing nearly 40 percent of each tooth's surface. The solution is simple — floss. Flossing gives you access to the whole tooth and shields you from gum disease.*

## 30 Saturday

## 31 Sunday

## Notes:

## The 3-cent cure for heart disease

Studies show that low doses of daily aspirin are as good — or even better — at preventing another stroke or heart attack as high doses for people with advanced heart disease or who have had a stroke. The low-dose aspirin helps keep the clotting factors or platelets from getting sticky and forming "clumps" in the blood vessels. Another benefit of low-dose aspirin is it causes fewer stomach problems than higher doses.

Be careful if you sometimes take the painkiller ibuprofen, like Motrin or Advil. A new study found that one dose of ibuprofen taken before your daily aspirin reduces aspirin's ability to help your blood vessels. Fortunately, other painkillers, like acetaminophen, didn't lower aspirin's effect so you may have other options to help ease pain.

Don't start taking aspirin every day without your doctor's advice. She can make sure daily aspirin is safe and effective for you.

| August | | | | | | |
|S|M|T|W|T|F|S|
|---|---|---|---|---|---|---|
| | | | | | |1|2|
|3|4|5|6|7|8|9|
|10|11|12|13|14|15|16|
|17|18|19|20|21|22|23|
|24|25|26|27|28|29|30|
|31|

| September | | | | | | |
|S|M|T|W|T|F|S|
|---|---|---|---|---|---|---|
| |1|2|3|4|5|6|
|7|8|9|10|11|12|13|
|14|15|16|17|18|19|20|
|21|22|23|24|25|26|27|
|28|29|30|

| October | | | | | | |
|S|M|T|W|T|F|S|
|---|---|---|---|---|---|---|
| | | |1|2|3|4|
|5|6|7|8|9|10|11|
|12|13|14|15|16|17|18|
|19|20|21|22|23|24|25|
|26|27|28|29|30|31|

# September

*Double-knit polyester has one of the highest sun protection factors. Wool jersey, plain polyester, and polyester/cotton blends are also protective.*

## 1 Monday
*Labor Day*

## 2 Tuesday

## 3 Wednesday

## 4 Thursday

## 5 Friday

*Did you know shaking too much salt on your food could cancel out the calcium in your glass of milk? Sodium competes with calcium for absorption. This means too much sodium can cause calcium to pass right through your body without being absorbed.*

# September  2003

*Water trapped in your ear canal after swimming can harbor bacteria and fungi, which can infect your ear. The next time you swim let vinegar come to the rescue. Mix one part vinegar to five parts lukewarm water, and put several drops of the mixture in your ear three times a day.*

## 6 Saturday

## 7 Sunday
*Grandparent's Day*

## Notes:

## Concentrate to make pain go away

You close your mind to pain. You try to think about escaping to an exotic, sun-drenched beach while the dentist grinds on your sensitive tooth. Escape tactics may not be the most effective way of coping with pain. Studies recommend concentrating on the location, quality, and intensity of painful sensations. You might actually prolong your discomfort by trying to stop thinking about these sensations.

Researchers speculate that monitoring painful sensations makes it easier to notice lessening of the pain. Suppression seems to weaken feelings of control and even decreases a person's ability to enjoy pleasant sensations immediately after a painful experience. Distraction doesn't seem to work as well as monitoring painful feelings, but it's better than suppressing them altogether.

Try concentrating on the painful sensations the next time you're uncomfortable. You might be pleasantly surprised.

| August | | | | | | | | September | | | | | | | October | | | | | | |
|---|---|---|---|---|---|---|---|---|---|---|---|---|---|---|---|---|---|---|---|---|---|
| S | M | T | W | T | F | S | | S | M | T | W | T | F | S | | S | M | T | W | T | F | S |
| | | | | | 1 | 2 | | | 1 | 2 | 3 | 4 | 5 | 6 | | | | | 1 | 2 | 3 | 4 |
| 3 | 4 | 5 | 6 | 7 | 8 | 9 | | 7 | 8 | 9 | 10 | 11 | 12 | 13 | | 5 | 6 | 7 | 8 | 9 | 10 | 11 |
| 10 | 11 | 12 | 13 | 14 | 15 | 16 | | 14 | 15 | 16 | 17 | 18 | 19 | 20 | | 12 | 13 | 14 | 15 | 16 | 17 | 18 |
| 17 | 18 | 19 | 20 | 21 | 22 | 23 | | 21 | 22 | 23 | 24 | 25 | 26 | 27 | | 19 | 20 | 21 | 22 | 23 | 24 | 25 |
| 24 | 25 | 26 | 27 | 28 | 29 | 30 | | 28 | 29 | 30 | | | | | | 26 | 27 | 28 | 29 | 30 | 31 | |
| 31 | | | | | | | | | | | | | | | | | | | | | |

# September

*Put your pizza on a diet. Blot the surface with a paper napkin to soak up fat and order vegetable toppings instead of extra cheese, pepperoni, or ground beef.*

## 8 Monday

## 9 Tuesday

## 10 Wednesday

## 11 Thursday
*Patriots' Day*

## 12 Friday

*Add Epsom salt to your first-aid kit. It comes in handy for a variety of ailments. You can reduce the swelling of scrapes and insect bites with a warm Epsom salt compress. Or use a cold compress to soothe an insect bite's sting. A warm Epsom salt bath also relieves muscle aches and pains.*

# September  2003

*Sick of monkeying around with dry hair? Mash a banana with a teaspoon of almond oil
and rub the mixture into your hair. Leave it there for 20 minutes, then rinse.*

## 13 Saturday

## 14 Sunday

## Notes:

## Make the most of bone-saving minerals

If you're over 50, you need 1,200 milligrams of calcium every day to prevent bone loss. But getting the recommended amount means little if your body isn't absorbing the calcium you eat and drink. Small changes in your diet can make big changes in the way your body uses calcium.

**Eat less protein**. Too much protein interferes with your body's ability to use calcium. Many people eat too much protein.

**Enrich your meals.** Your body absorbs calcium from food better than from supplements, so get your supply from foods, like fortified orange juice and yogurt.

**Get it at mealtime.** You're able to use more of the calcium from a glass of milk taken during a meal than as a lone snack.

**Pick produce.** Fruits and vegetables are full of potassium and magnesium. Without these minerals, your bones can't make use of calcium. Bananas and oranges are rich in both minerals.

| August | | | | | | | | September | | | | | | | | October | | | | | | |
|---|---|---|---|---|---|---|---|---|---|---|---|---|---|---|---|---|---|---|---|---|---|---|
| S | M | T | W | T | F | S | | S | M | T | W | T | F | S | | S | M | T | W | T | F | S |
| | | | | | 1 | 2 | | | 1 | 2 | 3 | 4 | 5 | 6 | | | | | | 1 | 2 | 3 | 4 |
| 3 | 4 | 5 | 6 | 7 | 8 | 9 | | 7 | 8 | 9 | 10 | 11 | 12 | 13 | | 5 | 6 | 7 | 8 | 9 | 10 | 11 |
| 10 | 11 | 12 | 13 | 14 | 15 | 16 | | 14 | 15 | 16 | 17 | 18 | 19 | 20 | | 12 | 13 | 14 | 15 | 16 | 17 | 18 |
| 17 | 18 | 19 | 20 | 21 | 22 | 23 | | 21 | 22 | 23 | 24 | 25 | 26 | 27 | | 19 | 20 | 21 | 22 | 23 | 24 | 25 |
| 24 | 25 | 26 | 27 | 28 | 29 | 30 | | 28 | 29 | 30 | | | | | | 26 | 27 | 28 | 29 | 30 | 31 | |
| 31 | | | | | | | | | | | | | | | | | | | | | | |

# September

*Arnica compresses on arthritic joints bring relief from soreness and stiffness because the herb acts like a painkiller, according to researchers.*

## 15 Monday

## 16 Tuesday

## 17 Wednesday

## 18 Thursday

## 19 Friday

*You can create a simple steam facial at home. Just boil some water, then remove the pot from the stove. Cover your head with a large towel to create a tent over the pot. Steam your face for five to 10 minutes. Add aromatic herbs to the water for a pleasant touch.*

# September  2003

*The death rate from cancer is 25 percent lower in Cheyenne, Wyo., than in Muncie, Ind. What's the difference? Cheyenne has one of the highest levels of selenium in the country, and Muncie, one of the lowest. Research shows that states rich in selenium suffer fewer cancer deaths.*

## 20 Saturday

## 21 Sunday

## Notes:

## Ditch your dry mouth 'dragon breath'

One of the top causes of bad breath is mouth dryness. When you don't have enough saliva, food particles and bacteria don't get washed away properly. Try these do's and don'ts to slay your "dragon breath."

**Chew sugar-free gum.** The chewing action and saliva work to rid your mouth of food particles and debris that may be causing your bad breath.

**Drink plenty of water.** It keeps your mouth clean and odor free. If you can't brush after a meal, swish water around in your mouth to wash away food particles.

**Avoid deodorizing sprays.** They can dry out your mouth and actually make your bad breath worse.

**Don't breathe through your mouth**. Unstuff your nose so you can breathe through it better. Mouth-breathing usually makes "morning breath" worse. That's because it dries out your mouth, which is already drier at night because fewer mouth movements produce less saliva.

| August | | | | | | |
|---|---|---|---|---|---|---|
| S | M | T | W | T | F | S |
| | | | | | 1 | 2 |
| 3 | 4 | 5 | 6 | 7 | 8 | 9 |
| 10 | 11 | 12 | 13 | 14 | 15 | 16 |
| 17 | 18 | 19 | 20 | 21 | 22 | 23 |
| 24 | 25 | 26 | 27 | 28 | 29 | 30 |
| 31 | | | | | | |

| September | | | | | | |
|---|---|---|---|---|---|---|
| S | M | T | W | T | F | S |
| | 1 | 2 | 3 | 4 | 5 | 6 |
| 7 | 8 | 9 | 10 | 11 | 12 | 13 |
| 14 | 15 | 16 | 17 | 18 | 19 | 20 |
| 21 | 22 | 23 | 24 | 25 | 26 | 27 |
| 28 | 29 | 30 | | | | |

| October | | | | | | |
|---|---|---|---|---|---|---|
| S | M | T | W | T | F | S |
| | | | 1 | 2 | 3 | 4 |
| 5 | 6 | 7 | 8 | 9 | 10 | 11 |
| 12 | 13 | 14 | 15 | 16 | 17 | 18 |
| 19 | 20 | 21 | 22 | 23 | 24 | 25 |
| 26 | 27 | 28 | 29 | 30 | 31 | |

# September

*Experts say going to church may help you live longer. One research team found that you could add seven years to your life by attending church more than once a week.*

## 22 Monday

## 23 Tuesday
*Autumn begins*

## 24 Wednesday

## 25 Thursday

## 26 Friday

*Cheese for dessert? Sounds bizarre, but it's a good idea. Sugary foods help bacteria in your mouth produce acid, which causes tooth decay. However, eating yellow cheese after a meal helps neutralize these acids. So if you can't resist that piece of cake after dinner, chew on some cheese, too.*

# September  2003

*Chiggers are mites that attack in bunches and attach larvae to skin folds. The result is intense itching and a rash. Your best defense is a hot bath. If you soak in hot water within hours of being exposed to chiggers, the larvae will be less likely to stick to your skin.*

## 27 Saturday
*Rosh Hashanah*

## 28 Sunday

## Notes:

## Kitchen remedies to prevent infection

Wounds can be a feeding ground for infections. When medicated wound dressings aren't available, these simple home remedies can help.

**Salt.** A solution of salt and water applied to sterile gauze, then placed over the wound, speeds healing and prevents infection. Add approximately three-quarters of a teaspoon of salt to three pints of sterile water for the best mixture.

**Honey**. It eases your sweet tooth and flavors your tea. Now honey could achieve a higher status in your medicine cabinet — right beside the hydrogen peroxide and bandages. The Egyptians discovered that applying honey to minor cuts actually helped the healing process.

**Sugar.** A paste of sugar and hydrogen peroxide applied to a new cut seems to halt the growth of bacteria. Researchers say sugar works against bacteria by removing water from around the wound since bacteria need water to grow.

| September | | | | | | |
|---|---|---|---|---|---|---|
| S | M | T | W | T | F | S |
| | 1 | 2 | 3 | 4 | 5 | 6 |
| 7 | 8 | 9 | 10 | 11 | 12 | 13 |
| 14 | 15 | 16 | 17 | 18 | 19 | 20 |
| 21 | 22 | 23 | 24 | 25 | 26 | 27 |
| 28 | 29 | 30 | | | | |

| October | | | | | | |
|---|---|---|---|---|---|---|
| S | M | T | W | T | F | S |
| | | | 1 | 2 | 3 | 4 |
| 5 | 6 | 7 | 8 | 9 | 10 | 11 |
| 12 | 13 | 14 | 15 | 16 | 17 | 18 |
| 19 | 20 | 21 | 22 | 23 | 24 | 25 |
| 26 | 27 | 28 | 29 | 30 | 31 | |

| November | | | | | | |
|---|---|---|---|---|---|---|
| S | M | T | W | T | F | S |
| | | | | | | 1 |
| 2 | 3 | 4 | 5 | 6 | 7 | 8 |
| 9 | 10 | 11 | 12 | 13 | 14 | 15 |
| 16 | 17 | 18 | 19 | 20 | 21 | 22 |
| 23 | 24 | 25 | 26 | 27 | 28 | 29 |
| 30 | | | | | | |

# September

*Barley was once used to treat boils, stomach disorders, and urinary tract infections. Today, whole-grain barley's high-fiber content, over 31 grams per cup, makes it a favorite health food.*

## 29 Monday

## 30 Tuesday

## 1 Wednesday

## 2 Thursday

## 3 Friday

*Research shows that relaxing and finding distractions from your problems will keep you in better spirits than if you dwell on them. Those who talk about their frustrations tend to become more negative. Music, art, and other mellow distractions are just the trick for fending off "the blues."*

# October  2003

## 4 Saturday

## 5 Sunday

## Notes:

## Strike out stress with B vitamins

Stress and anxiety often go hand-in-hand with digestion and absorption problems. This means your body may not be able to use all the nutrients you're taking in, and you could become vitamin deficient. B vitamins, in particular, are quickly used up during times of stress.

Several studies have found that people who take in the least amount of vitamin B12 are the most likely to suffer from depression and other mental problems, including anxiety. Another important B vitamin is B5 (pantothenic acid), sometimes called the "anti-stress" vitamin. It works to keep your adrenal gland functioning properly.

Foods high in B vitamins are peas, beans, lean meat, poultry, fish, whole-grain breads and cereals, bananas, avocados, cottage cheese, and potatoes.

| September | October | November |
|---|---|---|
| S M T W T F S | S M T W T F S | S M T W T F S |
| 1 2 3 4 5 6 | 1 2 3 4 | 1 |
| 7 8 9 10 11 12 13 | 5 6 7 8 9 10 11 | 2 3 4 5 6 7 8 |
| 14 15 16 17 18 19 20 | 12 13 14 15 16 17 18 | 9 10 11 12 13 14 15 |
| 21 22 23 24 25 26 27 | 19 20 21 22 23 24 25 | 16 17 18 19 20 21 22 |
| 28 29 30 | 26 27 28 29 30 31 | 23 24 25 26 27 28 29 |
| | | 30 |

# October

*You'll be safer when biking if you wear pink. The experts say neon pink is the color motorists can see most easily*

## 6 Monday
*Yom Kippur*

## 7 Tuesday

## 8 Wednesday

## 9 Thursday

## 10 Friday

*In a group of women undergoing outpatient surgery, half received a foot massage and painkillers after the procedure and half received just the painkillers. Those with the tickled tootsies said they felt less pain. So put up your feet and let someone rub your pain away.*

# October  2003

## 11 Saturday

## 12 Sunday

## Notes:

## Discover fiber's fabulous health benefits

Plants are made of two kinds of fiber — soluble and insoluble. Some plants have one type, while others have both.

Insoluble fiber doesn't dissolve in water. It's in whole grains, wheat bran, vegetables, seeds, peas, beans, and brown rice. By adding bulk, insoluble fiber speeds up your food's trip through your digestive system. That can help reduce your risk of colon cancer, diverticulosis, and appendicitis.

It also keeps your stools soft and your bowels moving regularly. That helps prevent constipation, hemorrhoids, hiatal hernia, and irritable bowel syndrome. Since the fiber absorbs water and swells, you feel full long after you eat it. That helps you lose weight.

Soluble fiber dissolves easily in water. It's found in fruits, vegetables, seeds, rye, oats, barley, rice bran, peas, and beans. Soluble fiber can help lower cholesterol and keep blood sugar levels on an even keel, even for people with diabetes.

| September | | | | | | |
|---|---|---|---|---|---|---|
| S | M | T | W | T | F | S |
| | 1 | 2 | 3 | 4 | 5 | 6 |
| 7 | 8 | 9 | 10 | 11 | 12 | 13 |
| 14 | 15 | 16 | 17 | 18 | 19 | 20 |
| 21 | 22 | 23 | 24 | 25 | 26 | 27 |
| 28 | 29 | 30 | | | | |

| October | | | | | | |
|---|---|---|---|---|---|---|
| S | M | T | W | T | F | S |
| | | | 1 | 2 | 3 | 4 |
| 5 | 6 | 7 | 8 | 9 | 10 | 11 |
| 12 | 13 | 14 | 15 | 16 | 17 | 18 |
| 19 | 20 | 21 | 22 | 23 | 24 | 25 |
| 26 | 27 | 28 | 29 | 30 | 31 | |

| November | | | | | | |
|---|---|---|---|---|---|---|
| S | M | T | W | T | F | S |
| | | | | | | 1 |
| 2 | 3 | 4 | 5 | 6 | 7 | 8 |
| 9 | 10 | 11 | 12 | 13 | 14 | 15 |
| 16 | 17 | 18 | 19 | 20 | 21 | 22 |
| 23 | 24 | 25 | 26 | 27 | 28 | 29 |
| 30 | | | | | | |

# October

*Women over 65 who walk or exercise regularly have fewer respiratory infections than those who don't.*

## 13 Monday
*Columbus Day*

## 14 Tuesday

## 15 Wednesday

## 16 Thursday
*National Boss Day*

## 17 Friday

*Studies show that naps can improve performance and increase alertness — for as long as 10 hours after a one- or two-hour nap and six hours after a 45-minute nap.*

# October  2003

## 18 Saturday

## 19 Sunday

## Notes:

## Rescue wrists from repetitive strain injury

If your work or hobby involves repeating a certain motion with your hands, tendons in your wrist can swell, pinching a nerve and causing pain. With these hints at your fingertips, you can prevent these repetitive strain injuries hands down.

- Take short breaks every half hour when doing work that requires extensive use of your hands.
- Stretch your hands during rest periods.
- Don't keep your hands in one position or bend your wrists for long periods of time.
- Use your whole hand and all of your fingers, instead of just your thumb and index finger, to pick up objects.
- Never sleep on your hands.
- Hold the steering wheel gently when driving.
- Use a foam pad for wrist support when typing or using a computer.
- Don't rest your wrists on the keyboard. Keep your wrists even. Don't bend them up or down.

| September | | | | | | | | October | | | | | | | November | | | | | |
|---|---|---|---|---|---|---|---|---|---|---|---|---|---|---|---|---|---|---|---|---|---|
| S | M | T | W | T | F | S | | S | M | T | W | T | F | S | S | M | T | W | T | F | S |
| | 1 | 2 | 3 | 4 | 5 | 6 | | | | | 1 | 2 | 3 | 4 | | | | | | | 1 |
| 7 | 8 | 9 | 10 | 11 | 12 | 13 | | 5 | 6 | 7 | 8 | 9 | 10 | 11 | 2 | 3 | 4 | 5 | 6 | 7 | 8 |
| 14 | 15 | 16 | 17 | 18 | 19 | 20 | | 12 | 13 | 14 | 15 | 16 | 17 | 18 | 9 | 10 | 11 | 12 | 13 | 14 | 15 |
| 21 | 22 | 23 | 24 | 25 | 26 | 27 | | 19 | 20 | 21 | 22 | 23 | 24 | 25 | 16 | 17 | 18 | 19 | 20 | 21 | 22 |
| 28 | 29 | 30 | | | | | | 26 | 27 | 28 | 29 | 30 | 31 | | 23 | 24 | 25 | 26 | 27 | 28 | 29 |
| | | | | | | | | | | | | | | | 30 | | | | | | |

# October

*The caffeine in one cup of coffee can increase your need for calcium by 30 to 50 milligrams for the day.*

## 20 Monday

## 21 Tuesday

## 22 Wednesday

## 23 Thursday

## 24 Friday

*Raw fish contains a substance that destroys thiamin, an important B vitamin. So if you enjoy sushi, you may want to boost your thiamin intake. Mild symptoms of a thiamin deficiency include irritability, tiredness, and sleep disturbances. Good sources of thiamin include oatmeal, black beans, and pecans.*

# October  2003

*As many as 80 percent of us underestimate the number of calories we eat, sometimes by as much as 800 calories a day. One possible reason for this is that some of us don't accurately judge how much food we put on our plates.*

## 25 Saturday

## 26 Sunday
*Daylight Saving Time ends*

## Notes:

## Lower your risk of gum disease

Gum disease, or gingivitis, affects almost 90 percent of Americans over age 65. It often stems from poor oral hygiene and is usually preventable. Here's how you can protect your teeth and gums.

- **Brush.** Twice a day is standard fare for most people, but brushing after any sweet or sticky snack makes good dental sense. Use a soft toothbrush and small circles, paying particular attention to the gum line, where most plaque grows. Hold the bristles at a 45-degree angle to your teeth.

- **Floss.** Use waxed or unwaxed dental floss at least once a day to clean between your teeth. Gently move the floss up and down around each tooth.

- **Swish.** Prescription mouthwashes containing chlorhexidine seem to be effective in preventing gingivitis. Ask your dentist about these products.

- **Chew.** Enjoy a piece of sugarless gum. Chewing increases your saliva, which is your mouth's first line of defense against plaque.

| September | | | | | | |
|---|---|---|---|---|---|---|
| S | M | T | W | T | F | S |
| | 1 | 2 | 3 | 4 | 5 | 6 |
| 7 | 8 | 9 | 10 | 11 | 12 | 13 |
| 14 | 15 | 16 | 17 | 18 | 19 | 20 |
| 21 | 22 | 23 | 24 | 25 | 26 | 27 |
| 28 | 29 | 30 | | | | |

| October | | | | | | |
|---|---|---|---|---|---|---|
| S | M | T | W | T | F | S |
| | | | 1 | 2 | 3 | 4 |
| 5 | 6 | 7 | 8 | 9 | 10 | 11 |
| 12 | 13 | 14 | 15 | 16 | 17 | 18 |
| 19 | 20 | 21 | 22 | 23 | 24 | 25 |
| 26 | 27 | 28 | 29 | 30 | 31 | |

| November | | | | | | |
|---|---|---|---|---|---|---|
| S | M | T | W | T | F | S |
| | | | | | | 1 |
| 2 | 3 | 4 | 5 | 6 | 7 | 8 |
| 9 | 10 | 11 | 12 | 13 | 14 | 15 |
| 16 | 17 | 18 | 19 | 20 | 21 | 22 |
| 23 | 24 | 25 | 26 | 27 | 28 | 29 |
| 30 | | | | | | |

# October

*Getting 1,000 to 1,300 milligrams of calcium a day can reduce depression, bloating, back pain, irritability, and headaches associated with PMS.*

## 27 Monday

## 28 Tuesday

## 29 Wednesday

## 30 Thursday

## 31 Friday
*Halloween*

*Fenugreek, a bitter-tasting legume, has been used throughout history for thousands of ailments — everything from settling a gassy stomach to soothing inflamed skin. Now, health experts say fenugreek may help diabetics lower their blood sugar and "bad" cholesterol.*

# November  2003

*If you don't cook an egg long enough to set the yolk, Salmonella bacteria may still be alive.
Approximately one egg in 20,000 contains the potentially deadly bacteria.*

## 1 Saturday

## 2 Sunday

## Notes:

## Secrets to snuff out snoring

Before you give up the fight against snoring, make sure you've taken the following steps:

**Lose weight.** Carrying extra pounds causes soft tissue to accumulate in your throat. The tissue blocks your air passages and leads to snoring.

**Avoid alcohol and tranquilizers.** Anything that works as a sedative, like alcohol or even most antihistamines, causes your tissues to relax and can contribute to snoring.

**Stop smoking.** Smokers tend to snore.

**Don't sleep on your back.** To prompt you to roll over on your side or stomach, sew a tennis ball into the back of your pajama top.

**Prop up the head of your bed.** You may be able to breathe a little easier with your head elevated. Propping up the whole upper part of your bed works better than adding extra pillows. Pillows can cause you to bend your neck, which closes your airways more and makes snoring worse.

| October | | | | | | | | November | | | | | | | | December | | | | | | |
|---|---|---|---|---|---|---|---|---|---|---|---|---|---|---|---|---|---|---|---|---|---|---|
| S | M | T | W | T | F | S | | S | M | T | W | T | F | S | | S | M | T | W | T | F | S |
| | | | 1 | 2 | 3 | 4 | | | | | | | | 1 | | | 1 | 2 | 3 | 4 | 5 | 6 |
| 5 | 6 | 7 | 8 | 9 | 10 | 11 | | 2 | 3 | 4 | 5 | 6 | 7 | 8 | | 7 | 8 | 9 | 10 | 11 | 12 | 13 |
| 12 | 13 | 14 | 15 | 16 | 17 | 18 | | 9 | 10 | 11 | 12 | 13 | 14 | 15 | | 14 | 15 | 16 | 17 | 18 | 19 | 20 |
| 19 | 20 | 21 | 22 | 23 | 24 | 25 | | 16 | 17 | 18 | 19 | 20 | 21 | 22 | | 21 | 22 | 23 | 24 | 25 | 26 | 27 |
| 26 | 27 | 28 | 29 | 30 | 31 | | | 23 | 24 | 25 | 26 | 27 | 28 | 29 | | 28 | 29 | 30 | 31 | | | |
| | | | | | | | | 30 | | | | | | | | | | | | | | |

# November

*A sugar-filled diet increases your risk of urinary tract infections.*

## 3 Monday

## 4 Tuesday
*Election Day*

## 5 Wednesday

## 6 Thursday

## 7 Friday

*Borborygmi — it's the sound your intestines make right before you politely excuse yourself for having a "growling stomach." Swallowed air, the type of food you have eaten in the last 24 hours, and how full your intestines are with liquid and food all play a part in whether your "stomach" talks.*

# November  2003

*Briskly shoveling light snow can burn as many calories as playing a tennis match. Using your arms and legs muscles to lift the weight of the snow increases your heart rate. Be sure to check with your doctor before you decide to shovel your driveway if you have heart problems.*

## 8 Saturday

## 9 Sunday

## Notes:

## Fatty foods that are good for you

A fatty fish may save your life — and here's why. Seafood contains omega-3 fatty acids, which can reduce your risk of heart disease. These fatty acids reduce the clumping of platelets in the blood and lessen the risk of coronary spasms. Experts say eating just one 3-ounce serving of fatty fish a week cuts your risk of heart disease by as much as 50 to 70 percent.

Salmon is a great source of omega-3, and you can also find high levels in tuna, mackerel, and herring. These fish either eat marine algae, which is rich in omega-3 fatty acids, or gobble up other smaller fish that ate the algae.

If you're an absolute landlubber who can't stand fish, you can get some omega-3 by eating flaxseed; walnuts; and collard, turnip, and mustard greens.

If you're an absolute landlubber who can't stand fish, you can get some omega-3's by eating flaxseed and walnuts and cooking with canola oil. Other good sources include dark green, leafy vegetables like collard, turnip, and mustard greens; spinach; arugula; kale; Swiss chard; certain types of lettuce; and purslane, a hard-to-find green used in Mediterranean salads.

| October | | | | | | |
|---|---|---|---|---|---|---|
| S | M | T | W | T | F | S |
| | | | | 1 | 2 | 3 | 4 |
| 5 | 6 | 7 | 8 | 9 | 10 | 11 |
| 12 | 13 | 14 | 15 | 16 | 17 | 18 |
| 19 | 20 | 21 | 22 | 23 | 24 | 25 |
| 26 | 27 | 28 | 29 | 30 | 31 | |

| November | | | | | | |
|---|---|---|---|---|---|---|
| S | M | T | W | T | F | S |
| | | | | | | 1 |
| 2 | 3 | 4 | 5 | 6 | 7 | 8 |
| 9 | 10 | 11 | 12 | 13 | 14 | 15 |
| 16 | 17 | 18 | 19 | 20 | 21 | 22 |
| 23 | 24 | 25 | 26 | 27 | 28 | 29 |
| 30 | | | | | | |

| December | | | | | | |
|---|---|---|---|---|---|---|
| S | M | T | W | T | F | S |
| | 1 | 2 | 3 | 4 | 5 | 6 |
| 7 | 8 | 9 | 10 | 11 | 12 | 13 |
| 14 | 15 | 16 | 17 | 18 | 19 | 20 |
| 21 | 22 | 23 | 24 | 25 | 26 | 27 |
| 28 | 29 | 30 | 31 | | | |

# November

*Adults who eat breakfast every day tend to weigh less and have lower cholesterol levels.*

## 10 Monday

## 11 Tuesday
*Veterans' Day*

## 12 Wednesday

## 13 Thursday

## 14 Friday

*A new brain imaging test may help doctors diagnose Alzheimer's disease. Until now, a brain autopsy was the only way to tell the difference between Alzheimer's and other dementias. This new test may allow diagnosis of Alzheimer's in people who are living.*

# November  2003

*Give Thanks*

*Researchers made some surprising discoveries about preparing food with alcohol. Many dishes retained at least half of the original amount of alcohol even after cooking. Up to 80 percent of the original amount of alcohol remained in the Cherries Jubilee and Grand Marnier sauce.*

## 15 Saturday

## 16 Sunday

## Notes:

## Relieve headache pain without drugs

If you like the smell of green apples, you may be able to reduce the pain of migraine headaches. A study of 50 "migraineurs" found that those who liked the smell of green apples reported less severe headaches when they sniffed this scent.

The herb feverfew has been used to prevent and treat headaches for more than 2,000 years. Researchers say its leaves contain chemicals that reduce the inflammation and muscle spasms associated with migraine headaches. You can buy feverfew preparations at a health or nutrition store. Check the label to be sure the preparation you buy contains at least 0.2 percent parthenolide, the main ingredient that reduces the pain and frequency of migraines.

What's more, researchers in Germany found that peppermint oil was as effective as acetaminophen in reducing headache pain. A mixture of 10 percent peppermint oil in ordinary alcohol — rubbed over the temples and forehead — brought pain relief within 15 minutes.

| | October | | | | | | | | | November | | | | | | | | | December | | | | | | |
|---|---|---|---|---|---|---|---|---|---|---|---|---|---|---|---|---|---|---|---|---|---|---|---|---|---|
| S | M | T | W | T | F | S | | S | M | T | W | T | F | S | | S | M | T | W | T | F | S |
| | | | 1 | 2 | 3 | 4 | | | | | | | | 1 | | | 1 | 2 | 3 | 4 | 5 | 6 |
| 5 | 6 | 7 | 8 | 9 | 10 | 11 | | 2 | 3 | 4 | 5 | 6 | 7 | 8 | | 7 | 8 | 9 | 10 | 11 | 12 | 13 |
| 12 | 13 | 14 | 15 | 16 | 17 | 18 | | 9 | 10 | 11 | 12 | 13 | 14 | 15 | | 14 | 15 | 16 | 17 | 18 | 19 | 20 |
| 19 | 20 | 21 | 22 | 23 | 24 | 25 | | 16 | 17 | 18 | 19 | 20 | 21 | 22 | | 21 | 22 | 23 | 24 | 25 | 26 | 27 |
| 26 | 27 | 28 | 29 | 30 | 31 | | | 23 | 24 | 25 | 26 | 27 | 28 | 29 | | 28 | 29 | 30 | 31 | | | |
| | | | | | | | | 30 | | | | | | | | | | | | | |

# November

*People who take vitamin E supplements
cut their risk of cataracts in half.*

## 17 Monday

## 18 Tuesday

## 19 Wednesday

## 20 Thursday

## 21 Friday

*A researcher studying "thermal therapy" suggests people at risk for heart disease should take
a low-heat sauna — 140 degrees F — for a 15-minute session, three to five times each week
and resting for 30 minutes afterward. A dry, moderately warm sauna might help improve
blood vessel and heart function.*

# November  2003

*Hospital patients with a view of a natural setting recovered from surgery nearly a day faster than patients who could only see a brick wall, according to one study. They even needed less painkilling medicine.*

## 22 Saturday

## 23 Sunday

## Notes:

## No apologies needed for aging brains

Health researchers once thought people lost massive numbers of brain cells as they got older. Not so. Brain cells do shrink or die off gradually, beginning in young adulthood. In fact, by the time you are 80, your brain is about 5 percent smaller. But this is a small loss, and you can compensate for it by increasing the connections between your brain cells.

These connections, called synapses, provide communication pathways. Every time you learn something new, you build a new connection or strengthen an existing one. The more you learn as you age, the stronger your web of synapses becomes.

Some changes in mental abilities do occur as you get older. You may have some memory problems, but your ability to recognize information remains the same as younger people. Yet, if asked to recall meaningless information or unimportant events, the older you are, the more errors you'll probably make.

| October | | | | | | | | November | | | | | | | | December | | | | | | |
|---|---|---|---|---|---|---|---|---|---|---|---|---|---|---|---|---|---|---|---|---|---|---|
| S | M | T | W | T | F | S | | S | M | T | W | T | F | S | | S | M | T | W | T | F | S |
| | | | 1 | 2 | 3 | 4 | | | | | | | | 1 | | | 1 | 2 | 3 | 4 | 5 | 6 |
| 5 | 6 | 7 | 8 | 9 | 10 | 11 | | 2 | 3 | 4 | 5 | 6 | 7 | 8 | | 7 | 8 | 9 | 10 | 11 | 12 | 13 |
| 12 | 13 | 14 | 15 | 16 | 17 | 18 | | 9 | 10 | 11 | 12 | 13 | 14 | 15 | | 14 | 15 | 16 | 17 | 18 | 19 | 20 |
| 19 | 20 | 21 | 22 | 23 | 24 | 25 | | 16 | 17 | 18 | 19 | 20 | 21 | 22 | | 21 | 22 | 23 | 24 | 25 | 26 | 27 |
| 26 | 27 | 28 | 29 | 30 | 31 | | | 23 | 24 | 25 | 26 | 27 | 28 | 29 | | 28 | 29 | 30 | 31 | | | |
| | | | | | | | | 30 | | | | | | | | | | | | | | |

# November

*Don't sniff moldy foods. You can inhale the mold spores and develop respiratory problems.*

## 24 Monday

## 25 Tuesday

## 26 Wednesday

## 27 Thursday
*Thanksgiving*

## 28 Friday

*Milk's calcium may help you sidestep a stroke. The men in one study who drank more than 16 ounces of milk a day were half as likely to suffer a stroke as the men who didn't drink milk or got their calcium from a nondairy source, such as supplements.*

# November  2003

*Dog allergens are not made up of dog hair, like cat allergens. Instead, the problem substances are saliva, skin, and urine. Since dog hair is not the offender, long-haired dogs cause no more allergic rhinitis symptoms than short-haired dogs.*

## 29 Saturday

## 30 Sunday

## Notes:

## Triumph over colds and flu

Even though a cold and the flu are quite different, they share some symptoms and treatments for home care.

**Stay fluid.** If you have a fever, you need extra liquid to keep from dehydrating. Fluids also help thin secretions from your lungs so you can cough them up. Eight to 10 cups of liquid a day should do it. Most people find hot drinks more soothing than cold ones.

**Gargle.** One-half teaspoon of salt stirred into a cup of warm water makes a soothing gargle. Another effective gargle is strong, brewed tea — warm or cold.

**Steam it up.** Hot, moist air can temporarily clear stuffy nasal passages. Take a hot shower or use a humidifier.

**Soothe your aches.** To comfort your aching back and muscles, try a heating pad or warm compress. You can make a quick compress by soaking a towel in hot water and wringing it out.

| November | | | | | | | December | | | | | | | January | | | | | | |
|---|---|---|---|---|---|---|---|---|---|---|---|---|---|---|---|---|---|---|---|---|
| S | M | T | W | T | F | S | S | M | T | W | T | F | S | S | M | T | W | T | F | S |
| | | | | | | 1 | | 1 | 2 | 3 | 4 | 5 | 6 | | | | | | 1 | 2 | 3 |
| 2 | 3 | 4 | 5 | 6 | 7 | 8 | 7 | 8 | 9 | 10 | 11 | 12 | 13 | 4 | 5 | 6 | 7 | 8 | 9 | 10 |
| 9 | 10 | 11 | 12 | 13 | 14 | 15 | 14 | 15 | 16 | 17 | 18 | 19 | 20 | 11 | 12 | 13 | 14 | 15 | 16 | 17 |
| 16 | 17 | 18 | 19 | 20 | 21 | 22 | 21 | 22 | 23 | 24 | 25 | 26 | 27 | 18 | 19 | 20 | 21 | 22 | 23 | 24 |
| 23 | 24 | 25 | 26 | 27 | 28 | 29 | 28 | 29 | 30 | 31 | | | | 25 | 26 | 27 | 28 | 29 | 30 | 31 |
| 30 | | | | | | | | | | | | | | | | | | | | |

# December

*The top disease-fighting fruits and vegetables are prunes, blueberries, blackberries, kale, strawberries, raisins, raspberries, oranges, plums, red grapes, and beets.*

## 1 Monday

## 2 Tuesday

## 3 Wednesday

## 4 Thursday

## 5 Friday

*A sudden, stressful event raises a man's heart rate higher and keeps it raised longer than a woman's heart rate. Some researchers think this physical response explains why men seem "programmed" to walk away from emotional disputes with their wives or girlfriends. It may be that men truly "can't handle it."*

# December  2003

*Men who have enlarged prostates should avoid certain drugs and foods. Over-the-counter medicines that can worsen symptoms include many cough and cold remedies, hay fever products, bronchodilators, and appetite suppressants. Spicy foods, alcohol, coffee, and other caffeinated drinks can also cause problems.*

## 6 Saturday

## 7 Sunday

## Notes:

## 4 ways to minimize your potbelly

To avoid that "Buddha belly" look — and the discomfort that comes with it — try these no-nonsense remedies:

- Don't overeat, especially in the evening. Too much food in your stomach puts pressure on your stomach muscles and pushes them out. When you go to bed with a full stomach, your abdominal muscles relax, making it easy for the food to exert pressure on these muscles. Do this often, and you'll soon have a perfect potbelly.

- Suck it in. Holding your stomach in whenever you think of it is a great stomach exercise. It also helps you sit and stand straighter and avoid back pain.

- Be sure to stretch your hamstrings (the muscles at the back of your thighs) after you exercise. Tight hamstrings can cause you to develop a slight swayback and make your potbelly more noticeable.

- Exercise your stomach and lower back muscles regularly. This improves posture and helps prevent your stomach from sticking out.

| November | | | | | | | | December | | | | | | | | January | | | | | | |
|---|---|---|---|---|---|---|---|---|---|---|---|---|---|---|---|---|---|---|---|---|---|---|
| S | M | T | W | T | F | S | | S | M | T | W | T | F | S | | S | M | T | W | T | F | S |
| | | | | | | 1 | | | 1 | 2 | 3 | 4 | 5 | 6 | | | | | | | 1 | 2 | 3 |
| 2 | 3 | 4 | 5 | 6 | 7 | 8 | | 7 | 8 | 9 | 10 | 11 | 12 | 13 | | 4 | 5 | 6 | 7 | 8 | 9 | 10 |
| 9 | 10 | 11 | 12 | 13 | 14 | 15 | | 14 | 15 | 16 | 17 | 18 | 19 | 20 | | 11 | 12 | 13 | 14 | 15 | 16 | 17 |
| 16 | 17 | 18 | 19 | 20 | 21 | 22 | | 21 | 22 | 23 | 24 | 25 | 26 | 27 | | 18 | 19 | 20 | 21 | 22 | 23 | 24 |
| 23 | 24 | 25 | 26 | 27 | 28 | 29 | | 28 | 29 | 30 | 31 | | | | | 25 | 26 | 27 | 28 | 29 | 30 | 31 |
| 30 | | | | | | | | | | | | | | | | | | | | | |

# December

*Make sure you get enough shut-eye. Even a slight sleep shortage can cause depression in some people.*

## 8 Monday

## 9 Tuesday

## 10 Wednesday

## 11 Thursday

## 12 Friday

*One out of every 10 Americans has some hearing loss. The Better Hearing Institute in Washington reports that you probably have a hearing problem if you shout in conversations, turn the TV or radio too loud, ask people to repeat themselves, favor one ear, or strain to hear.*

# December  2003

*Oatmeal can fill your stomach and warm your soul at the same time. Researchers say complex carbohydrates, like those found in oatmeal, can trigger the increase of serotonin in your brain, which can raise your spirits. In fact, one bowl of oatmeal can improve your mood for several hours.*

## 13 Saturday

## 14 Sunday

## Notes:

## Warning signs of a stroke

Stroke strikes terror into the hearts of many older adults. Nearly three-fourths of all strokes occur in people over age 65. Strokes cause more disability than any other factor, and they take the lives of hundreds of thousands of people each year. A stroke deprives the brain of oxygen and damages brain cells. Receiving immediate medical attention can determine whether or not you survive. Unfortunately, most people don't know the warning signs of a stroke. The most common symptoms are:

- Sudden dimness or loss of vision in one eye.
- Weakness or numbness of the arm, leg, or face on one side of the body.
- Slurred speech, loss of speech, or trouble understanding speech.
- Sudden unexplained headache.
- Dizziness or falling for no reason.

If you experience any of these symptoms, seek help right away. Getting help quickly could save your life.

| November | | | | | | | December | | | | | | | January | | | | | | |
|---|---|---|---|---|---|---|---|---|---|---|---|---|---|---|---|---|---|---|---|---|
| S | M | T | W | T | F | S | S | M | T | W | T | F | S | S | M | T | W | T | F | S |
| | | | | | | 1 | | 1 | 2 | 3 | 4 | 5 | 6 | | | | | 1 | 2 | 3 |
| 2 | 3 | 4 | 5 | 6 | 7 | 8 | 7 | 8 | 9 | 10 | 11 | 12 | 13 | 4 | 5 | 6 | 7 | 8 | 9 | 10 |
| 9 | 10 | 11 | 12 | 13 | 14 | 15 | 14 | 15 | 16 | 17 | 18 | 19 | 20 | 11 | 12 | 13 | 14 | 15 | 16 | 17 |
| 16 | 17 | 18 | 19 | 20 | 21 | 22 | 21 | 22 | 23 | 24 | 25 | 26 | 27 | 18 | 19 | 20 | 21 | 22 | 23 | 24 |
| 23 | 24 | 25 | 26 | 27 | 28 | 29 | 28 | 29 | 30 | 31 | | | | 25 | 26 | 27 | 28 | 29 | 30 | 31 |
| 30 | | | | | | | | | | | | | | | | | | | | |

# December

*"One sip of this will bathe the drooping spirits in delight, beyond the bliss of dreams." — John Milton, author of Paradise Lost, on tea*

## 15 Monday

## 16 Tuesday

## 17 Wednesday

## 18 Thursday

## 19 Friday

*You can buy special creams made with capsaicin — the active ingredient in chili peppers — to relieve arthritis pain. Rub a pea-sized amount into your sore joint three to four times a day. Wear rubber gloves when handling the cream, and be careful not to get any near your face.*

# December  2003

*Men who drink two or three cups of coffee a day have fewer gallstones than noncoffee drinkers. And men who drink more than four are even better off. It doesn't matter how you brew the coffee, but it has to be caffeinated to provide the benefit.*

## 20 Saturday
*Hanukkah begins*

## 21 Sunday

## Notes:

## Suppress your appetite with OJ

Drink a glass of fructose-rich orange juice before a meal, and you'll eat fewer calories during the meal and still feel comfortably full. Fructose is a very sweet sugar found in fruit.

In a Yale study, overweight men who drank a glass of orange juice a half-hour to one hour before eating consumed nearly 300 fewer calories at lunch. Overweight women consumed an average of 431 fewer midday calories. Their intakes were compared with similarly overweight men and women who drank plain water before lunch.

Since the juice was about 200 calories, the calories saved was 100 to 230 calories per meal. If only for one meal a day, that still adds up to a savings of 700 calories a week or 36,400 calories a year. But remember — the diet benefit doesn't carry over to soft drinks sweetened with high-fructose corn syrup.

| November | | | | | | | | December | | | | | | | January | | | | | | |
|---|---|---|---|---|---|---|---|---|---|---|---|---|---|---|---|---|---|---|---|---|---|---|
| S | M | T | W | T | F | S | | S | M | T | W | T | F | S | | S | M | T | W | T | F | S |
| | | | | | | 1 | | | 1 | 2 | 3 | 4 | 5 | 6 | | | | | | | 1 | 2 | 3 |
| 2 | 3 | 4 | 5 | 6 | 7 | 8 | | 7 | 8 | 9 | 10 | 11 | 12 | 13 | | 4 | 5 | 6 | 7 | 8 | 9 | 10 |
| 9 | 10 | 11 | 12 | 13 | 14 | 15 | | 14 | 15 | 16 | 17 | 18 | 19 | 20 | | 11 | 12 | 13 | 14 | 15 | 16 | 17 |
| 16 | 17 | 18 | 19 | 20 | 21 | 22 | | 21 | 22 | 23 | 24 | 25 | 26 | 27 | | 18 | 19 | 20 | 21 | 22 | 23 | 24 |
| 23 | 24 | 25 | 26 | 27 | 28 | 29 | | 28 | 29 | 30 | 31 | | | | | 25 | 26 | 27 | 28 | 29 | 30 | 31 |
| 30 | | | | | | | | | | | | | | | | | | | | | | |

# December

*Avoid sugary breath mints. Try chomping on parsley, anise, or fennel seeds for naturally sweet breath.*

## 22 Monday
*Winter begins*

## 23 Tuesday

## 24 Wednesday

## 25 Thursday
*Christmas*

## 26 Friday
*Kwanzaa begins*

*It's a startling statistic — 80 percent of all diabetics are overweight. Obesity has become the single most important cause of Type 2 diabetes. If you already have Type 2 diabetes, a recent study found that losing as little as 5 pounds can help reverse it.*

# December  2003

*If you want to get an accurate reading on your blood pressure, before your next doctor's visit lay off the caffeine, cigarettes, alcohol — and water. A recent study found that seniors experience a rise in blood pressure after drinking just two cups of water.*

## 27 Saturday

## 28 Sunday

## Notes:

## Spare your life by losing your spare tire

The spare tire you carry with you in your car is a safety precaution. But the other spare tire you carry with you — the one around your belly — is a safety hazard.

Apple-shaped people, those with stomach fat, have a greater risk of heart disease than pear-shaped people, those with fat around the hips and thighs. And people with more stomach fat have higher amounts of triglycerides in the blood after eating a high-fat meal. The extra stomach fat seems to influence how the body processes fat from the meal.

High levels of trigylcerides can lead to hardening of the arteries and result in strokes and heart attacks. Apple-shaped people also have unfavorable blood levels of cholesterol, insulin, and saturated fats compared with people who have less stomach fat.

People with a lot of stomach fat should begin a safe weight loss program to reduce the risk of serious health problems.

| November | December | January |
|---|---|---|
| S M T W T F S | S M T W T F S | S M T W T F S |
|            1 |   1  2  3  4  5  6 |           1  2  3 |
| 2  3  4  5  6  7  8 | 7  8  9 10 11 12 13 | 4  5  6  7  8  9 10 |
| 9 10 11 12 13 14 15 | 14 15 16 17 18 19 20 | 11 12 13 14 15 16 17 |
| 16 17 18 19 20 21 22 | 21 22 23 24 25 26 27 | 18 19 20 21 22 23 24 |
| 23 24 25 26 27 28 29 | 28 29 30 31 | 25 26 27 28 29 30 31 |
| 30 | | |

# December

*Eat just 3 ounces of peanuts a day and you've gotten half the amount of folate you need to fight an artery-damaging chemical called homocysteine.*

## 29 Monday

## 30 Tuesday

## 31 Wednesday
*New Year's Eve*

## 1 Thursday
*New Year's Day*

## 2 Friday

*Regular exercise can do wonders for your body, your attitude, and your stroke risk. A study of more than 5,000 diabetic nurses showed that walking regularly was an effective way to cut stroke risk. That's great news because brisk walking is something that almost anyone can do.*

# January  2004

*Medieval stonemasons carved the shape of the strawberry into the pillars of churches as a symbol of perfection. One cup of berries has a full day's requirement of vitamin C and fills you up with over 3 grams of fiber. In addition, strawberries are rich in folate and potassium.*

## 3 Saturday

## 4 Sunday

## Notes:

## Take the bite out of frostbite

When the temperature drops, take the following steps to reduce your risk of frostbite.

**Get out of the wind.** Wind makes you lose heat five times faster than still weather, and rain or snow will chill your body 25 times faster than dry skies.

**Drink plenty of water and other liquids.** Dehydration is by far the number one bodily cause of frostbite.

**Take regular breaks.** Don't strain too hard when working, playing, or seeking shelter from the cold. Fatigue and sweating raise your risk of frostbite.

**Avoid alcohol and cigarettes.** Alcohol makes you think you're warm when you're not, so your body doesn't shiver. Shivering is a natural way to produce heat.

**Choose clothes carefully.** Make sure your clothes are well-insulated, dry, and not too tight. And don't forget your hat and scarf — 80 percent of your body heat is lost from your head and neck.

# Discover the secret to good nutrition

You can't live without vitamins and minerals. Your body needs a certain amount each day. Missing your daily quota occasionally won't hurt, but if you shortchange yourself on a regular basis, you put yourself in danger.

Luckily, you'll find plenty of vitamins and minerals in grains, legumes, fruits, seafood, lean meats, vegetables, and other foods. By making smart food choices, you'll protect yourself from a long list of diseases, including cancer, heart disease, arthritis, cataracts, and depression — just to name a few.

To give you a good idea of the importance of vitamins and minerals, pay special attention to the "Benefits" and "Signs of deficiencies" for each nutrient included in the following charts. Then scan the list of foods, choose your favorites, and see how well you're meeting your DRI or Dietary Reference Intakes. These new guidelines replace the RDA — Recommended Dietary Allowances.

| Nutrient | What it is | Benefits | Signs of deficiency | DRI Women Age 51+ | DRI Men Age 51+ |
|----------|-----------|----------|---------------------|-------------------|------------------|
| Phosphorus | Mineral | • builds new cells<br>• produces energy | • tiredness<br>• loss of appetite<br>• pain in bones | 700 mg | 700 mg |

| Sources of phosphorus | Amount | Phosphorus content |
|-----------------------|--------|--------------------|
| Snacks, trail mix, regular, with chocolate chips, salted nuts and seeds | 1 cup | 565 mg |
| Breakfast items, biscuit with egg and sausage | 1 biscuit | 490 mg |
| Fast foods, pancakes with butter and syrup | 2 pancakes | 476 mg |
| Halibut, Atlantic and Pacific, cooked, dry heat | 1/2 fillet | 453 mg |
| Cheese, ricotta, part skim milk | 1 cup | 450 mg |
| Duck, domesticated, meat only, cooked, roasted | 1/2 duck | 449 mg |
| Barley, pearled, raw | 1 cup | 442 mg |
| Salmon, sockeye, cooked, dry heat | 1/2 fillet | 428 mg |
| Soybeans, mature cooked, boiled, without salt | 1 cup | 421 mg |
| Sardine, Atlantic, canned in oil, drained solids with bone | 3 oz | 417 mg |
| Pollock, walleye, cooked, dry heat | 3 oz | 410 mg |
| Cheese, ricotta, whole milk | 1 cup | 389 mg |
| Milk shakes, thick chocolate | 11 fl oz | 378 mg |
| Fast foods, cheeseburger, regular, double patty, plain | 1 sandwich | 374 mg |
| Seeds, sunflower seed kernels, dry roasted, with salt added | 1/4 cup | 370 mg |
| Tuna salad | 1 cup | 365 mg |
| Milk shakes, thick vanilla | 11 fl oz | 360 mg |

| Nutrient | What it is | Benefits | Signs of deficiency | DRI Women Age 51+ | DRI Men Age 51+ |
|---|---|---|---|---|---|
| Magnesium | Mineral | • builds bones and teeth<br>• relaxes muscles<br>• makes proteins<br>• helps body use nutrients<br>• steadies heart rhythm | • tiredness<br>• loss of appetite<br>• muscle cramps and twitches<br>• convulsions<br>• depression<br>• confusion | 320 mg | 420 mg |

| Sources of magnesium | Amount | Magnesium content |
|---|---|---|
| Snacks, trail mix, regular, with chocolate chips, salted nuts and seeds | 1 cup | 235 mg |
| Halibut, Atlantic and Pacific, cooked, dry heat | 1/2 fillet | 170 mg |
| Spinach, canned, drained solids | 1 cup | 163 mg |
| Barley, pearled, raw | 1 cup | 158 mg |
| Seeds, pumpkin and squash seed kernels, roasted, with salt added | 1 oz (142 seeds) | 151 mg |
| Soybeans, mature cooked, boiled, without salt | 1 cup | 148 mg |
| Beans, white, mature seeds, canned | 1 cup | 134 mg |
| Cereals ready-to-eat, KELLOGG, KELLOGG'S ALL-BRAN | 1/2 cup | 129 mg |
| Fast foods, taco, beef | 1 large | 108 mg |
| Beans, navy, mature seeds, cooked, boiled, without salt | 1 cup | 107 mg |
| Fast foods, taco, beef | 1 large | 108 mg |
| Beans, navy, mature seeds, cooked, boiled, without salt | 1 cup | 107 mg |
| Lima beans, immature seeds, frozen, baby, cooked, boiled, drained, without salt | 1 cup | 101 mg |
| Artichokes, (globe or French), cooked, boiled, drained, without salt | 1 cup | 94 mg |
| Lima beans, large, mature seeds, canned | 1 cup | 94 mg |
| Okra, frozen, cooked, boiled, drained, without salt | 1 cup | 94 mg |
| Halibut, Atlantic and Pacific, cooked, dry heat | 3 oz | 91 mg |
| Muffins, oat bran | 1 muffin | 89 mg |
| Beans, baked, canned, with pork and sweet sauce | 1 cup | 86 mg |

| Nutrient | What it is | Benefits | Signs of deficiency | DRI Women Age 51+ | DRI Men Age 51+ |
|---|---|---|---|---|---|
| Calcium | Mineral | •builds bones and teeth<br><br>•contracts muscles and nerves<br><br>•sends nerve messages<br><br>•controls blood pressure | •bone loss (osteoporosis) | 1,200 mg | 1,200 mg |

| Sources of calcium | Amount | Calcium content |
|---|---|---|
| Cheese, ricotta, part skim milk | 1 cup | 669 mg |
| Milk shakes, thick vanilla | 11 fl oz | 457 mg |
| Yogurt, plain, low fat, 12 grams protein per 8 ounces | 8-oz container | 415 mg |
| Collards, frozen, chopped, cooked, boiled, drained, without salt | 1 cup | 357 mg |
| Rhubarb, frozen, cooked, with sugar | 1 cup | 348 mg |
| Yogurt, fruit, low fat, 10 grams protein per 8 ounces | 8-oz container | 345 mg |
| Sardine, Atlantic, canned in oil, drained solids with bone | 3 oz | 325 mg |
| Cereals ready-to-eat, GENERAL MILLS, BASIC 4 | 1 cup | 310 mg |
| Milk, low fat or skim, fluid, 0-1% milkfat, with added vitamin A | 1 cup | 300 mg |
| Spinach, frozen, chopped or leaf, cooked, boiled, drained, without salt | 1 cup | 277 mg |
| Cereals ready-to-eat, GENERAL MILLS, TOTAL | 3/4 cup | 258 mg |
| Turnip greens, frozen, cooked, boiled, drained, without salt | 1 cup | 249 mg |
| Cereals ready-to-eat, GENERAL MILLS, TOTAL Raisin Bran | 1 cup | 238 mg |
| Biscuits, plain or buttermilk, prepared from recipe | 4" biscuit | 237 mg |
| Cheese, provolone | 1 oz | 214 mg |
| Cheese, mozzarella, part skim milk, low moisture | 1 oz | 207 mg |
| Fast foods, sundae, hot fudge | 1 sundae | 207 mg |
| Cheese, cheddar | 1 oz | 204 mg |
| Salmon, pink, canned, solids with bone and liquid | 3 oz | 181 mg |

| Nutrient | What it is | Benefits | Signs of deficiency | DRI Women Age 51+ | DRI Men Age 51+ |
|---|---|---|---|---|---|
| Potassium | Mineral | • sends nerve messages<br>• relaxes nerves<br>• maintains chemical balances<br>• steadies blood pressure | • dehydration<br>• weakness<br>• trouble concentrating | 3,500 mg | 3,500 mg |

| Sources of potassium | Amount | Potassium content |
|---|---|---|
| Beet greens, cooked, boiled, drained, without salt | 1 cup | 1,309 mg |
| Beans, white, mature seeds, canned | 1 cup | 1,189 mg |
| Fast foods, potato, french fried in vegetable oil | 1 large | 1,164 mg |
| Dates, domestic, natural and dry | 1 cup | 1,161 mg |
| Raisins, seedless | 1 cup | 1,089 mg |
| Soybeans, green, cooked, boiled, drained, without salt | 1 cup | 970 mg |
| Potatoes, au gratin, home-prepared from recipe using butter | 1 cup | 970 mg |
| Lima beans, large, mature seeds, cooked, boiled, without salt | 1 cup | 955 mg |
| Halibut, Atlantic and Pacific, cooked, dry heat | 1/2 fillet | 916 mg |
| Squash, winter, all varieties, cooked, baked, without salt | 1 cup | 896 mg |
| Plantains, raw | 1 medium | 896 mg |
| Soybeans, mature cooked, boiled, without salt | 1 cup | 886 mg |
| Nuts, chestnuts, European, roasted | 1 cup | 847 mg |
| Spinach, cooked, boiled, drained, without salt | 1 cup | 839 mg |
| Sweet potato, canned, vacuum pack | 1 cup | 796 mg |
| Papayas, raw | 1 papaya | 781 mg |
| Sauce, pasta, spaghetti/marinara, ready-to-serve | 1 cup | 738 mg |
| Bananas, raw | 1 banana | 467 mg |
| Vegetable juice cocktail, canned | 1 cup | 467 mg |
| Melons, honeydew, raw | 1 cup | 461 mg |

| Nutrient | What it is | Benefits | Signs of deficiency | DRI Women Age 51+ | DRI Men Age 51+ |
|---|---|---|---|---|---|
| Iron | Trace mineral | •carries oxygen throughout body<br><br>•produces energy | •weakness<br>•pale skin<br><br>•trouble concentrating | 8 mg | 8 mg |

| Sources of iron | Amount | Iron content |
|---|---|---|
| Clam, mixed species, canned, drained solids | 3 oz | 24 mg |
| Cereals ready-to-eat, GENERAL MILLS, TOTAL Raisin Bran | 1 cup | 18 mg |
| Cereals ready-to-eat, GENERAL MILLS, TOTAL Corn Flakes | 1-1/3 cup | 18 mg |
| Cereals ready-to-eat, GENERAL MILLS, TOTAL | 3/4 cup | 18 mg |
| Cereals ready-to-eat, KELLOGG, KELLOGG'S PRODUCT 19 | 1 cup | 18 mg |
| Cereals ready-to-eat, KELLOGG'S FROSTED MINI-WHEATS, bite size | 1 cup | 15 mg |
| Cereals, CREAM OF WHEAT, regular, cooked with water, without salt | 1 cup | 10 mg |
| Cereals, MALT-O-MEAL, plain and chocolate, cooked with water, without salt | 1 cup | 10 mg |
| Soybeans, mature cooked, boiled, without salt | 1 cup | 9 mg |
| Cereals, CREAM OF WHEAT, mix'n eat, plain, prepared with water | 1 packet | 8 mg |
| Cereals, MALT-O-MEAL, plain and chocolate, cooked with water, without salt | 1 cup | 10 mg |
| Soybeans, mature cooked, boiled, without salt | 1 cup | 9 mg |
| Cereals, CREAM OF WHEAT, mix'n eat, plain, prepared with water | 1 packet | 8 mg |
| Snacks, CHEX mix | 1 oz (about 2/3 cup) | 7 mg |
| Lentils, mature seeds, cooked, boiled, without salt | 1 cup | 7 mg |
| Spinach, cooked, boiled, drained, without salt | 1 cup | 6 mg |
| WORTHINGTON FOODS, MORNINGSTAR FARMS Burger Crumbles | 1 cup | 6 mg |
| Cereals, oats, instant, fortified, plain, prepared with water | 1 packet | 6 mg |

| Nutrient | What it is | Benefits | Signs of deficiency | DRI Women Age 51+ | DRI Men Age 51+ |
|---|---|---|---|---|---|
| Manganese mineral | Trace | •produces energy <br><br> •builds bones and joints | •unknown | 2-11 mg | 2-11 mg |

| Sources of manganese | Amount | Manganese content |
|---|---|---|
| Pineapple, canned, juice pack, solids and liquids | 1 cup | 3 mg |
| Cereals ready-to-eat, KELLOGG, KELLOGG'S ALL-BRAN | 1/2 cup | 3 mg |
| Cereals ready-to-eat, GENERAL MILLS, HONEY NUT CLUSTERS | 1 cup | 3 mg |
| Barley, pearled, raw | 1 cup | 3 mg |
| Pineapple, raw | 1 cup | 3 mg |
| Oat bran, cooked | 1 cup | 2 mg |
| Rice, white, long-grain, regular, raw, enriched | 1 cup | 2 mg |
| Cereals, WHEATENA, cooked with water | 1 cup | 2 mg |
| Spaghetti, whole-wheat, cooked | 1 cup | 2 mg |
| Okra, frozen, cooked, boiled, drained, without salt | 1 cup | 2 mg |
| Blackberries, raw | 1 cup | 2 mg |
| Spinach, frozen, chopped or leaf, cooked, boiled, drained, without salt | 1 cup | 2 mg |
| Rice, brown, long-grain, cooked | 1 cup | 2 mg |
| Nuts, hazelnuts or filberts | 1 oz | 2 mg |
| Chickpeas (garbanzo beans), mature seeds, cooked, boiled, without salt | 1 cup | 2 mg |
| Nuts, chestnuts, European, roasted | 1 cup | 2 mg |
| Spinach, cooked, boiled, drained, without salt | 1 cup | 2 mg |
| Raspberries, frozen, red, sweetened | 1 cup | 2 mg |
| Cereals ready-to-eat, FROSTED KELLOGG'S MINI-WHEATS, bite size | 1 cup | 2 mg |

| Nutrient | What it is | Benefits | Signs of deficiency | DRI Women Age 51+ | DRI Men Age 51+ |
|---|---|---|---|---|---|
| Selenium | Trace mineral | •makes thyroid hormones<br><br>•fights free radicals<br><br>•strengthens immune system | •muscle weakness and pain<br><br>•cataracts<br><br>•heart trouble | 55 mcg | 55 mcg |

| Sources of selenium | Amount | Nutrient content |
|---|---|---|
| Nuts, brazil nuts, dried, unblanched | 1 oz (6-8 nuts) | 839 mcg |
| Turkey, all classes, giblets, cooked, simmered, some giblet fat | 1 cup | 321 mcg |
| Chicken, broilers or fryers, giblets, cooked, simmered | 1 cup | 136 mcg |
| Nuts, mixed nuts, oil roasted, with peanuts, with salt added | 1 oz | 119 mcg |
| Fast foods, fish sandwich, with tartar sauce and cheese | 1 sandwich | 89 mcg |
| Tuna salad | 1 cup | 84 mcg |
| Barley, pearled, raw | 1 cup | 75 mcg |
| Halibut, Atlantic and Pacific, cooked, dry heat | 1/2 fillet | 74 mcg |
| Flounder or sole, cooked, dry heat | 1 fillet | 74 mcg |
| Fast foods, shrimp, breaded and fried | 6-8 shrimp | 68 mcg |
| Tuna, light, canned in water, drained solids | 3 oz | 68 mcg |
| Swordfish, cooked, dry heat | 1 piece | 65 mcg |
| Haddock, cooked, dry heat | 1 fillet | 61 mcg |
| Salmon, sockeye, cooked, dry heat | 1/2 fillet | 59 mcg |
| Oyster, eastern, cooked, breaded and fried | 3 oz | 57 mcg |
| Turkey, all classes, meat only, cooked, roasted | 1 cup | 52 mcg |
| Bread stuffing, bread, dry mix, prepared | 1/2 cup | 50 mcg |
| Duck, domesticated, meat only, cooked, roasted | 1/2 duck | 50 mcg |
| Fast foods, chili con carne | 1 cup | 44 mcg |

| Nutrient | What it is | Benefits | Signs of deficiency | DRI Women Age 51+ | DRI Men Age 51+ |
|---|---|---|---|---|---|
| Zinc | Trace mineral | •produces energy<br><br>•makes DNA<br><br>•helps body use vitamin A<br><br>•fights free radicals<br><br>•heals wounds<br><br>•boosts immune system | •diarrhea<br><br>•infections<br><br>•loss of appetite<br><br>•weight loss<br><br>•unhealed wounds | 8 mg | 11 mg |

| Sources of zinc | Amount | Nutrient content |
|---|---|---|
| Oyster, eastern, cooked, breaded and fried | 3 oz | 74 mg |
| Cereals ready-to-eat, GENERAL MILLS, TOTAL Corn Flakes | 1-1/3 cup | 15 mg |
| Cereals ready-to-eat, GENERAL MILLS, TOTAL Raisin Bran | 1 cup | 15 mg |
| Beans, baked, canned, with pork and tomato sauce | 1 cup | 15 mg |
| Beef, chuck, blade roast, separable lean only, trimmed to 1/4" fat, all grades, cooked, braised | 3 oz | 9 mg |
| Crab, Alaska king, cooked, moist heat | 3 oz | 6 mg |
| Fast foods, hamburger, regular, double patty, with condiments | 1 sandwich | 6 mg |
| Trail mix, regular, with chocolate chips, salted nuts and seeds | 1 cup | 5 mg |
| Fast foods, submarine sandwich, with roast beef | 1 sandwich, 6" roll | 5 mg |
| Turkey, all classes, meat only, cooked, roasted | 1 cup | 4 mg |
| Barley, pearled, raw | 1 cup | 4 mg |
| Cereals ready-to-eat, GENERAL MILLS, CHEERIOS | 1 cup | 4 mg |
| Soup, vegetable, canned, chunky, ready-to-serve, commercial | 1 cup | 3 mg |
| Refried beans, canned | 1 cup | 3 mg |
| Candies, semisweet chocolate | 1 cup | 3 mg |
| Fast foods, taco salad | 1-1/2 cups | 3 mg |
| Chickpeas (garbanzo beans), canned | 1 cup | 3 mg |
| Lentils, mature seeds, cooked, boiled, without salt | 1 cup | 3 mg |
| Yogurt, plain, skim milk, 13 grams protein per 8 ounces | 8-oz container | 2 mg |

| Nutrient | What it is | Benefits | Signs of deficiency | DRI Women Age 51+ | DRI Men Age 51+ |
|---|---|---|---|---|---|
| Vitamin A (Retinol, or Retinoic acid) | Fat-soluble vitamin | • controls eyesight<br>• builds new cells<br>• protects skin and mucous membranes<br>• fights infection and free radicals | • weak immune system<br>• night blindness<br>• diarrhea<br>• dry skin and hair | 800 RE<br><br>4,000 IU | 1,000 RE<br>or<br>5,000 IU |

| Sources of vitamin A | Amount | Nutrient content |
|---|---|---|
| Carrots, cooked, boiled, drained, without salt | 1 cup | 38,304 IU |
| Sweet potato, cooked, baked in skin, without salt | 1 potato | 31,860 IU |
| Beef, variety meats and by-products, liver, cooked, pan-fried | 3 oz | 30,689 IU |
| Carrot juice, canned | 1 cup | 25,833 IU |
| Sweet potato, canned, vacuum pack | 1 cup | 20,357 IU |
| Carrots, raw | 1 carrot | 20,253 IU |
| Vegetables, mixed, canned, drained solids | 1 cup | 18,985 IU |
| Spinach, cooked, boiled, drained, without salt | 1 cup | 14,742 IU |
| Pie, pumpkin, prepared from recipe | 1 piece | 11,833 IU |
| Collards, frozen, chopped, cooked, boiled, drained, without salt | 1 cup | 10,168 IU |
| Peppers, sweet, red, raw | 1 cup | 8,493 IU |
| Squash, winter, butternut, frozen, cooked, drained, without salt | 1 cup | 8,014 IU |
| Soup, chicken vegetable, canned, chunky, ready-to-serve | 1 cup | 5,990 IU |
| Melons, cantaloupe, raw | 1 cup | 5,158 IU |
| Apricots, canned, juice pack, with skin, solids and liquids | 1 cup | 4,126 IU |
| Soup, bean with ham, canned, chunky, ready-to-serve, commercial | 1 cup | 3,951 IU |
| Beef stew, canned entree | 1 cup | 3,860 IU |
| Broccoli, frozen, chopped, cooked, boiled, drained, without salt | 1 cup | 3,481 IU |
| Vegetable juice cocktail, canned | 1 cup | 2,831 IU |

| Nutrient | What it is | Benefits | Signs of deficiency | DRI Women Age 51+ | DRI Men Age 51+ |
|---|---|---|---|---|---|
| Vitamin D (Calciferol) | Fat-soluble vitamin | •builds bones<br><br>•controls calcium and phosphorous levels in your body | •joint pain<br><br>•bowing legs<br><br>•muscle spasms | 10 mcg or 400 IU (15 mcg if age 70+) | 10 mcg or 400 IU (15 mcg if age 70+) |

| Sources of vitamin D | Amount | Nutrient content |
|---|---|---|
| Salmon, cooked | 3-1/2 oz | 360 IU |
| Mackerel, cooked | 3-1/2 oz | 345 IU |
| Sardines, canned in oil, drained | 3-1/2 oz | 270 IU |
| Milk, nonfat, dry, instant, CARNATION | 1/3 cup | 100 IU |
| Milk, nonfat, reduced fat, and whole, vitamin D fortified | 1 cup | 98 IU |
| Cereals, ready to eat, HEALTHY CHOICE, ALMOND CRUNCH WITH RAISINS | 1 cup | 80 IU |
| Margarine, fortified | 1 tbsp | 60 IU |
| Cereals, ready to eat, POST, Raisin Bran | 1 cup | 60 IU |
| Cereals, ready to eat, POST, FRUIT & FIBRE w/dates, raisins & walnuts | 1 cup | 60 IU |
| Cereal grain bars, fortified | 1 each | 50 IU |
| Pudding, prepared from mix and made with vitamin D fortified milk | 1/2 cup | 50 IU |
| Cereals, ready to eat, KELLOGG, KELLOGG'S ALL BRAN | 1/2 cup | 40 IU |
| Cereals, ready to eat, POST, GRAPE-NUTS | 1/2 cup | 40 IU |
| Cereals, ready to eat, KELLOGG'S, PRODUCT 19 | 1 cup | 40 IU |
| Cereals, ready to eat, KELLOGG'S, RICE KRISPIES | 1-1/4 cups | 40 IU |
| Cereals, ready to eat, KELLOGG'S, COMPLETE BRAN FLAKES | 3/4 cup | 40 IU |
| Milk, evaporated, canned, CARNATION | 2 tbsp | 24 IU |
| Egg substitute, BETTER'N EGG, frozen, MORNING-STAR FARMS | 1/4 cup | 22 IU |
| Fast food, TACO BELL, Mexican pizza | 1 serving | 10 IU |

| Nutrient | What it is | Benefits | Signs of deficiency | DRI Women Age 51+ | DRI Men Age 51+ |
|---|---|---|---|---|---|
| Vitamin E (Tocopherol) | Fat-soluble vitamin | •fights free radicals<br><br>•leg cramps<br><br>•pale skin | •weakness | 15 mg or 22 IU | 15 mg or 22 IU |

| Sources of vitamin E | Amount | Nutrient content |
|---|---|---|
| Cereals ready-to-eat, GENERAL MILLS, TOTAL Raisin Bran | 1 cup | 30 mg |
| Seeds, sunflower seed kernels, dry roasted, with salt added | 1/4 cup | 16 mg |
| Nuts, almonds | 1 oz (24 nuts) | 7 mg |
| Oil, vegetable, sunflower, linoleic, (60% and over) | 1 tbsp | 7 mg |
| Cereals ready-to-eat, KELLOGG, KELLOGG'S COMPLETE WHEAT BRAN FLAKES | 3/4 cup | 5 mg |
| Turnip greens, frozen, cooked, boiled, drained, without salt | 1 cup | 5 mg |
| Fast foods, french toast sticks | 5 sticks | 4 mg |
| Oil, soybean, salad or cooking, (hydrogenated) and cottonseed | 1 tbsp | 4 mg |
| Peaches, canned, juice pack, solids and liquids | 1 cup | 4 mg |
| Tomato products, canned, sauce | 1 cup | 3 mg |
| Papayas, raw | 1 papaya | 3 mg |
| Pie, chocolate creme, commercially prepared | 1 piece | 3 mg |
| Broccoli, frozen, chopped, cooked, boiled, drained, without salt | 1 cup | 3 mg |
| Cereals ready-to-eat, GENERAL MILLS, HONEY NUT CLUSTERS | 1 cup | 3 mg |
| Breakfast items, biscuit with egg and sausage | 1 biscuit | 3 mg |
| Soup, tomato, canned, prepared with equal volume milk, commercial | 1 cup | 3 mg |
| Sweet rolls, cinnamon, commercially prepared with raisins | 1 roll | 3 mg |
| Asparagus, frozen, cooked, boiled, drained, without salt | 1 cup | 2 mg |
| Peanuts, all types, dry-roasted, without salt | 1 oz (approx 28) | 2 mg |

| Nutrient | What it is | Benefits | Signs of deficiency | DRI Women Age 51+ | DRI Men Age 51+ |
|---|---|---|---|---|---|
| B1 (Thiamin) | Water-soluble vitamin | •produces energy<br><br>•sends nerve messages<br><br>•brings on healthy appetite | •swollen and puffy skin (edema)<br>•tiredness<br>•depression<br>•trouble concentrating | 1.1 mg | 1.2 mg |

| Sources of vitamin B1 | Amount | Nutrient content |
|---|---|---|
| WORTHINGTON FOODS, MORNINGSTAR FARMS Burger Crumbles | 1 cup | 10 mg |
| Cereals ready-to-eat, GENERAL MILLS, TOTAL Raisin Bran | 1 cup | 2 mg |
| Cereals ready-to-eat, GENERAL MILLS, TOTAL | 3/4 cup | 2 mg |
| Cereals ready-to-eat, KELLOGG, KELLOGG'S PRODUCT 19 | 1 cup | 2 mg |
| Cereals ready-to-eat, GENERAL MILLS, TOTAL Corn Flakes | 1-1/3 cups | 2 mg |
| Fast foods, submarine sandwich, with cold cuts | 1 sandwich, 6" roll | 1 mg |
| Pork, fresh, loin, center loin (chops), bone-in, cooked, pan-fried | 3 oz | 1 mg |
| Pork, cured, ham, extra lean and regular, canned, roasted | 3 oz | 1 mg |
| Malted milk-flavor mix, chocolate, added nutrients, powder, prepared with milk | 1 cup | 1 mg |
| Trail mix, tropical | 1 cup | 1 mg |
| Cereals ready-to-eat, QUAKER, QUAKER OAT CINNAMON LIFE | 1 cup | 1 mg |
| Ham, sliced, extra lean, (approximately 5% fat) | 2 slices | 1 mg |
| Cereals ready-to-eat, KELLOGG, KELLOGG'S SPECIAL K | 1 cup | 1 mg |
| Breakfast items, biscuit with egg and sausage | 1 biscuit | 1 mg |
| English muffin, with egg, cheese, and Canadian bacon | 1 muffin | 0.4 mg |
| Bagels, plain, enriched, with calcium propionate (includes onion, poppy, sesame) | 4" bagel | 0.4 mg |
| Fast foods, submarine sandwich, with tuna salad | 1 sandwich, 6" roll | 0.4 mg |
| Fast foods, fish sandwich, with tartar sauce and cheese | 1 sandwich | 0.4 mg |
| Peas, green, frozen, cooked, boiled, drained, without salt | 1 cup | 0.4 mg |

| Nutrient | What it is | Benefits | Signs of deficiency | DRI Women Age 51+ | DRI Men Age 51+ |
|---|---|---|---|---|---|
| Vitamin B2 (Riboflavin) | Water-soluble vitamin | •produces energy<br><br>•helps vision<br><br>•builds new cells | •cracked lips<br><br>•skin rash<br><br>•trouble seeing in bright light | 1.1 mg | 1.3 mg |

| Sources of vitamin B2 | Amount | Nutrient content |
|---|---|---|
| HEALTHY CHOICE Spaghetti Bolognese, frozen entree | 1 package | 4 mg |
| Cereals ready-to-eat, KELLOGG, KELLOGG'S PRODUCT | 1 cup | 2 mg |
| Cereals ready-to-eat, GENERAL MILLS, TOTAL | 3/4 cup | 2 mg |
| Cereals ready-to-eat, GENERAL MILLS, KELLOGG'S Corn Flakes | 1-1/3 cup | 2 mg |
| Cereals ready-to-eat, GENERAL MILLS, TOTAL Raisin Bran | 1 cup | 2 mg |
| Fast foods, chili con carne | 1 cup | 1 mg |
| Fast foods, shrimp, breaded and fried | 6-8 shrimp | 1 mg |
| Fast food, chocolate shake | 16 fl oz | 1 mg |
| Cereals ready-to-eat, QUAKER, QUAKER OAT CINNAMON LIFE | 1 cup | 1 mg |
| Fast foods, hot dog, with corn flour coating (corn dog) | 1 corn dog | 1 mg |
| Fast foods, taco, beef | 1 large | 1 mg |
| Fast foods, pancakes with butter and syrup | 2 pancakes | 1 mg |
| Yogurt, plain, skim milk, 13 grams protein per 8 ounces | 8-oz container | 1 mg |
| Breakfast items, french toast with butter | 2 slices | 1 mg |
| Fast foods, tostada, with beans, beef, and cheese | 1 tostada | 0.4 mg |
| Cereals ready-to-eat, KELLOGG, KELLOGG'S Raisin Bran | 1 cup | 0.4 mg |
| Mushrooms, cooked, boiled, drained, without salt | 1 cup | 0.4 mg |
| Fast foods, English muffin, with egg, cheese, and Canadian bacon | 1 muffin | 0.4 mg |
| Milk, low fat, fluid, 1% milkfat, with added vitamin A | 1 cup | 0.4 mg |

| Nutrient | What it is | Benefits | Signs of deficiency | DRI Women Age 51+ | DRI Men Age 51+ |
|---|---|---|---|---|---|
| Vitamin B3 (Niacin) | Water-soluble vitamin | •produces energy<br><br>•builds DNA | •diarrhea<br><br>•black and smooth tongue<br><br>•skin rash<br><br>•trouble concentrating | 14 mg | 16 mg |

| Sources of vitamin B3 | Amount | Nutrient content |
|---|---|---|
| Cereals ready-to-eat, GENERAL MILLS, TOTAL Corn Flakes | 1-1/3 cups | 20 mg |
| Cereals ready-to-eat, GENERAL MILLS, TOTAL Raisin Bran | 1 cup | 20 mg |
| Tuna salad | 1 cup | 14 mg |
| Chicken, broilers or fryers, breast, meat only, cooked, roasted | 1/2 breast | 12 mg |
| Malted milk-flavor mix, chocolate, added nutrients, powder, prepared with milk | 1 cup | 11 mg |
| Salmon, sockeye, cooked, dry heat | 1/2 fillet | 10 mg |
| Chicken, canned, meat only, with broth | 5 oz | 9 mg |
| Cereals ready-to-eat, QUAKER, QUAKER OAT CINNAMON LIFE | 1 cup | 8 mg |
| Fast foods, cheeseburger, regular, double patty, with condiments and vegetables | 1 sandwich | 8 mg |
| Turkey, all classes, meat only, cooked, roasted | 1 cup | 7 mg |
| Fast foods, chicken, breaded and fried, boneless pieces, plain | 6 pieces | 7 mg |
| Cereals ready-to-eat, KELLOGG, KELLOGG'S SPECIAL K | 1 cup | 7 mg |
| Mushrooms, cooked, boiled, drained, without salt | 1 cup | 7 mg |
| Trail mix, regular, with chocolate chips, salted nuts and seeds | 1 cup | 6 mg |
| Fast foods, cheeseburger, regular, double patty and bun, plain | 1 sandwich | 6 mg |
| Fast foods, submarine sandwich, with roast beef | 1 sandwich, 6" roll | 6 mg |
| Fast foods, salad, vegetable, tossed, without dressing, with chicken | 1-1/2 cups | 6 mg |
| Salmon, pink, canned, solids with bone and liquid | 3 oz | 6 mg |
| Soup, chicken noodle, canned, chunky, ready-to-serve | 1 cup | 4 mg |

| Nutrient | What it is | Benefits | Signs of deficiency | DRI Women Age 51+ | DRI Men Age 51+ |
|---|---|---|---|---|---|
| Folate (Folic acid, Folacin) | Water-soluble vitamin | •makes and repairs DNA<br>•removes homo-cysteine from blood | •tiredness<br><br>•depression<br><br>•smooth and sore tongue<br><br>•digestion problems<br><br>•headaches | 400 mcg | 400 mcg |

| Sources of folate | Amount | Nutrient content |
|---|---|---|
| Cereals ready-to-eat, GENERAL MILLS, TOTAL | 3/4 cup | 675 mcg |
| Cereals ready-to-eat, GENERAL MILLS, Wheat CHEX | 1 cup | 407 mcg |
| Lentils, mature seeds, cooked, boiled, without salt | 1 cup | 358 mcg |
| Beans, pinto, mature seeds, cooked, boiled, without salt | 1 cup | 294 mcg |
| Chickpeas (garbanzo beans), mature seeds, cooked, boiled, without salt | 1 cup | 282 mcg |
| Cereals ready-to-eat, QUAKER, QUAKER OAT CINNAMON LIFE | 1 cup | 278 mcg |
| Okra, frozen, cooked, boiled, drained, without salt | 1 cup | 268 mcg |
| Spinach, cooked, boiled, drained, without salt | 1 cup | 262 mcg |
| Beans, navy, mature seeds, cooked, boiled, without salt | 1 cup | 254 mcg |
| WORTHINGTON FOODS, MORNINGSTAR FARMS BETTER'N BURGERS, frozen | 1 patty | 245 mcg |
| Asparagus, frozen, cooked, boiled, drained, without salt | 1 cup | 243 mcg |
| Beans, kidney, red, mature seeds, cooked, boiled, without salt | 1 cup | 230 mcg |
| Spinach, frozen, chopped or leaf, cooked, boiled, drained, without salt | 1 cup | 205 mcg |
| HEALTHY CHOICE Spaghetti Bolognese, frozen entree | 1 package | 203 mcg |
| Cereals ready-to-eat, KELLOGG, KELLOGG'S Raisin Bran | 1 cup | 199 mcg |
| Cereals ready-to-eat, KELLOGG, KELLOGG'S RICE KRISPIES | 1-1/4 cups | 197 mcg |
| Beans, great northern, mature seeds, cooked, boiled, without salt | 1 cup | 180 mcg |
| Cereals ready-to-eat, KELLOGG'S FROSTED MINI-WHEATS, bite size | 1 cup | 179 mcg |
| Collards, cooked, boiled, drained, without salt | 1 cup | 176 mcg |

| Nutrient | What it is | Benefits | Signs of deficiency | DRI Women Age 51+ | DRI Men Age 51+ |
|----------|-----------|----------|---------------------|-------------------|------------------|
| Vitamin B12 (Cobalamin) | Water-soluble vitamin | •makes new cells (especially red blood cells)<br><br>•protects nerves | •numbness in extremities<br><br>•muscle weakness<br>•weight loss<br>•depression<br>•smooth and sore tongue | 2.4 mcg | 2.4 mcg |

| Sources of vitamin B12 | Amount | Nutrient content |
|------------------------|--------|------------------|
| Clam, mixed species, canned, drained solids | 3 oz | 84 mcg |
| Oyster, eastern, cooked, breaded and fried | 3 oz | 13 mcg |
| Soup, clam chowder, New England, canned, prepared with equal volume milk, commercial | 1 cup | 10 mcg |
| Crab, Alaska king, cooked, moist heat | 3 oz | 10 mcg |
| Salmon, sockeye, cooked, dry heat | 1/2 fillet | 9 mcg |
| Cereals ready-to-eat, GENERAL MILLS, TOTAL Corn Flakes | 1-1/3 cups | 8 mcg |
| Cereals ready-to-eat, GENERAL MILLS, TOTAL | 3/4 cup | 8 mcg |
| Sardine, Atlantic, canned in oil, drained solids with bone | 3 oz | 8 mcg |
| Cereals ready-to-eat, GENERAL MILLS, TOTAL Raisin Bran | 1 cup | 6 mcg |
| Soup, PROGRESSO HEALTHY CLASSICS NEW ENGLAND CLAM CHOWDER, canned, ready-to-serve | 1 cup | 6 mcg |
| Cereals ready-to-eat, KELLOGG, KELLOGG'S PRODUCT 19 | 1 cup | 6 mcg |
| WORTHINGTON FOODS, MORNINGSTAR FARMS Burger Crumbles | 1 cup | 4 mcg |
| Fast foods, hamburger, large, double patty, with condiments and vegetables | 1 sandwich | 4 mcg |
| Tuna, light, canned in oil, drained solids | 3 oz | 2 mcg |
| Beef, round, eye of round, separable lean only, trimmed to 1/4" fat, all grades, cooked, roasted | 3 oz | 2 mcg |
| Beef, ground, extra lean, cooked, broiled, medium | 3 oz | 2 mcg |
| Fast foods, submarine sandwich, with roast beef | 1 sandwich, 6" roll | 2 mcg |
| Cereals ready-to-eat, KELLOGG, KELLOGG'S Raisin Bran | 1 cup | 2 mcg |
| Milk shakes, thick vanilla | 11 fl oz | 2 mcg |

| Nutrient | What it is | Benefits | Signs of deficiency | DRI Women Age 51+ | DRI Men Age 51+ |
|---|---|---|---|---|---|
| Vitamin B6 (Pyridoxine) | Water-soluble vitamin | • makes red blood cells<br><br>• builds proteins<br><br>• regulates blood sugar<br><br>• makes brain chemicals<br><br>• protects immune system | • fatigue<br><br>• poor moods<br><br>• smooth and sore tongue<br><br>• skin inflammation | 1.5 mg | 1.7 mg |

| Sources of vitamin B6 | Amount | Nutrient content |
|---|---|---|
| Cereals ready-to-eat, KELLOGG, KELLOGG'S PRODUCT | 1 cup | 2 mg |
| Cereals ready-to-eat, GENERAL MILLS, TOTAL Raisin Bran | 1 cup | 2 mg |
| Chickpeas (garbanzo beans), mature seeds, canned | 1 cup | 1 mg |
| Malted milk-flavor mix, chocolate, added nutrients, powder, prepared with milk | 1 cup | 1 mg |
| Tuna, yellowfin, fresh, cooked, dry heat | 3 oz | 1 mg |
| Cereals, oats, instant, fortified, plain, prepared with water | 1 packet | 1 mg |
| Potatoes, baked, flesh and skin, without salt | 1 potato | 1 mg |
| Bananas, raw | 1 banana | 1 mg |
| Turkey, all classes, meat only, cooked, roasted | 1 cup | 1 mg |
| Fast foods, potato, french fried in vegetable oil | 1 large | 1 mg |
| Chicken, broilers or fryers, breast, meat and skin, cooked, fried, batter | 1/2 breast | 1 mg |
| Cereals, CREAM OF WHEAT, mix'n eat, plain, prepared with water | 1 packet | 1 mg |
| Prune juice, canned | 1 cup | 1 mg |
| Fast foods, hamburger, large, double patty, with condiments and vegetables | 1 sandwich | 1 mg |
| Prunes, dried, stewed, without added sugar | 1 cup | 1 mg |
| WORTHINGTON FOODS, MORNINGSTAR FARMS Burger Crumbles | 1 cup | 1 mg |
| Haddock, cooked, dry heat | 1 fillet | 1 mg |
| Snacks, KELLOGG, KELLOGG'S NUTRI-GRAIN Cereal Bars, fruit | 1 bar | 1 mg |
| Chicken, canned, meat only, with broth | 5 oz | 0.5 mg |

# YEAR AT A GLANCE

## 2002

| January | February | March | April | May | June |
|---|---|---|---|---|---|
| S M T W T F S | S M T W T F S | S M T W T F S | S M T W T F S | S M T W T F S | S M T W T F S |
| 1 2 3 4 5 | 1 2 | 1 2 | 1 2 3 4 5 6 | 1 2 3 4 | 1 |
| 6 7 8 9 10 11 12 | 3 4 5 6 7 8 9 | 3 4 5 6 7 8 9 | 7 8 9 10 11 12 13 | 5 6 7 8 9 10 11 | 2 3 4 5 6 7 8 |
| 13 14 15 16 17 18 19 | 10 11 12 13 14 15 16 | 10 11 12 13 14 15 16 | 14 15 16 17 18 19 20 | 12 13 14 15 16 17 18 | 9 10 11 12 13 14 15 |
| 20 21 22 23 24 25 26 | 17 18 19 20 21 22 23 | 17 18 19 20 21 22 23 | 21 22 23 24 25 26 27 | 19 20 21 22 23 24 25 | 16 17 18 19 20 21 22 |
| 27 28 29 30 31 | 24 25 26 27 28 | 24 25 26 27 28 29 30 | 28 29 30 | 26 27 28 29 30 31 | 23 24 25 26 27 28 29 |
| | | 31 | | | 30 |

| July | August | September | October | November | December |
|---|---|---|---|---|---|
| S M T W T F S | S M T W T F S | S M T W T F S | S M T W T F S | S M T W T F S | S M T W T F S |
| 1 2 3 4 5 6 | 1 2 3 | 1 2 3 4 5 6 7 | 1 2 3 4 5 | 1 2 | 1 2 3 4 5 6 7 |
| 7 8 9 10 11 12 13 | 4 5 6 7 8 9 10 | 8 9 10 11 12 13 14 | 6 7 8 9 10 11 12 | 3 4 5 6 7 8 9 | 8 9 10 11 12 13 14 |
| 14 15 16 17 18 19 20 | 11 12 13 14 15 16 17 | 15 16 17 18 19 20 21 | 13 14 15 16 17 18 19 | 10 11 12 13 14 15 16 | 15 16 17 18 19 20 21 |
| 21 22 23 24 25 26 27 | 18 19 20 21 22 23 24 | 22 23 24 25 26 27 28 | 20 21 22 23 24 25 26 | 17 18 19 20 21 22 23 | 22 23 24 25 26 27 28 |
| 28 29 30 31 | 25 26 27 28 29 30 31 | 29 30 | 27 28 29 30 31 | 24 25 26 27 28 29 30 | 29 30 31 |

## 2003

| January | February | March | April | May | June |
|---|---|---|---|---|---|
| S M T W T F S | S M T W T F S | S M T W T F S | S M T W T F S | S M T W T F S | S M T W T F S |
| 1 2 3 4 | 1 | 1 | 1 2 3 4 5 | 1 2 3 | 1 2 3 4 5 6 7 |
| 5 6 7 8 9 10 11 | 2 3 4 5 6 7 8 | 2 3 4 5 6 7 8 | 6 7 8 9 10 11 12 | 4 5 6 7 8 9 10 | 8 9 10 11 12 13 14 |
| 12 13 14 15 16 17 18 | 9 10 11 12 13 14 15 | 9 10 11 12 13 14 15 | 13 14 15 16 17 18 19 | 11 12 13 14 15 16 17 | 15 16 17 18 19 20 21 |
| 19 20 21 22 23 24 25 | 16 17 18 19 20 21 22 | 16 17 18 19 20 21 22 | 20 21 22 23 24 25 26 | 18 19 20 21 22 23 24 | 22 23 24 25 26 27 28 |
| 26 27 28 29 30 31 | 23 24 25 26 27 28 | 23 24 25 26 27 28 29 | 27 28 29 30 | 25 26 27 28 29 30 31 | 29 30 |
| | | 30 31 | | | |

| July | August | September | October | November | December |
|---|---|---|---|---|---|
| S M T W T F S | S M T W T F S | S M T W T F S | S M T W T F S | S M T W T F S | S M T W T F S |
| 1 2 3 4 5 | 1 2 | 1 2 3 4 5 6 | 1 2 3 4 | 1 | 1 2 3 4 5 6 |
| 6 7 8 9 10 11 12 | 3 4 5 6 7 8 9 | 7 8 9 10 11 12 13 | 5 6 7 8 9 10 11 | 2 3 4 5 6 7 8 | 7 8 9 10 11 12 13 |
| 13 14 15 16 17 18 19 | 10 11 12 13 14 15 16 | 14 15 16 17 18 19 20 | 12 13 14 15 16 17 18 | 9 10 11 12 13 14 15 | 14 15 16 17 18 19 20 |
| 20 21 22 23 24 25 26 | 17 18 19 20 21 22 23 | 21 22 23 24 25 26 27 | 19 20 21 22 23 24 25 | 16 17 18 19 20 21 22 | 21 22 23 24 25 26 27 |
| 27 28 29 30 31 | 24 25 26 27 28 29 30 | 28 29 30 | 26 27 28 29 30 31 | 23 24 25 26 27 28 29 | 28 29 30 31 |
| | 31 | | | 30 | |

## 2004

| January | February | March | April | May | June |
|---|---|---|---|---|---|
| S M T W T F S | S M T W T F S | S M T W T F S | S M T W T F S | S M T W T F S | S M T W T F S |
| 1 2 3 | 1 2 3 4 5 6 7 | 1 2 3 4 5 6 | 1 2 3 | 1 | 1 2 3 4 5 |
| 4 5 6 7 8 9 10 | 8 9 10 11 12 13 14 | 7 8 9 10 11 12 13 | 4 5 6 7 8 9 10 | 2 3 4 5 6 7 8 | 6 7 8 9 10 11 12 |
| 11 12 13 14 15 16 17 | 15 16 17 18 19 20 21 | 14 15 16 17 18 19 20 | 11 12 13 14 15 16 17 | 9 10 11 12 13 14 15 | 13 14 15 16 17 18 19 |
| 18 19 20 21 22 23 24 | 22 23 24 25 26 27 28 | 21 22 23 24 25 26 27 | 18 19 20 21 22 23 24 | 16 17 18 19 20 21 22 | 20 21 22 23 24 25 26 |
| 25 26 27 28 29 30 31 | 29 | 28 29 30 31 | 25 26 27 28 29 30 | 23 24 25 26 27 28 29 | 27 28 29 30 |
| | | | | 30 31 | |

| July | August | September | October | November | December |
|---|---|---|---|---|---|
| S M T W T F S | S M T W T F S | S M T W T F S | S M T W T F S | S M T W T F S | S M T W T F S |
| 1 2 3 | 1 2 3 4 5 6 7 | 1 2 3 4 | 1 2 | 1 2 3 4 5 6 | 1 2 3 4 |
| 4 5 6 7 8 9 10 | 8 9 10 11 12 13 14 | 5 6 7 8 9 10 11 | 3 4 5 6 7 8 9 | 7 8 9 10 11 12 13 | 5 6 7 8 9 10 11 |
| 11 12 13 14 15 16 17 | 15 16 17 18 19 20 21 | 12 13 14 15 16 17 18 | 10 11 12 13 14 15 16 | 14 15 16 17 18 19 20 | 12 13 14 15 16 17 18 |
| 18 19 20 21 22 23 24 | 22 23 24 25 26 27 28 | 19 20 21 22 23 24 25 | 17 18 19 20 21 22 23 | 21 22 23 24 25 26 27 | 19 20 21 22 23 24 25 |
| 25 26 27 28 29 30 31 | 29 30 31 | 26 27 28 29 30 | 24 25 26 27 28 29 30 | 28 29 30 | 26 27 28 29 30 31 |
| | | | 31 | | |

# ADDRESSES

NAME_____

ADDRESS_____

_____

TELEPHONE_____ CELL _____

NAME_____

ADDRESS_____

_____

TELEPHONE_____ CELL _____

NAME_____

ADDRESS_____

_____

TELEPHONE_____ CELL _____

NAME_____

ADDRESS_____

_____

TELEPHONE_____ CELL _____

NAME_____

ADDRESS_____

_____

TELEPHONE_____ CELL _____

NAME_____

ADDRESS_____

_____

TELEPHONE_____ CELL _____